Psychiatry
and the Deaf

Discrimination Prohibited

Psychiatry and the Deaf

Edited by

John D. Rainer, M.D., *and* Kenneth Z. Altshuler, M.D.

Being a report of the Workshop for Psychiatrists on Extending Mental Health Services to the Deaf, sponsored by the New York State Psychiatric Institute and the New York University Center for Research and Training in Deafness Rehabilitation, April 7–8, 1967.

This workshop was supported by contract #VRA 67-32 from the Social and Rehabilitation Service, Department of Health, Education, and Welfare, Washington, D.C.

PLANNING COMMITTEE

Dr. John D. Rainer, New York State Psychiatric Institute
Dr. Kenneth Z. Altshuler, New York State Psychiatric Institute
Dr. Edna S. Levine, New York University
Dr. McCay Vernon, Michael Reese Hospital
Dr. Boyce R. Williams, U.S. Social and Rehabilitation Service
Dr. L. Deno Reed, U.S. Social and Rehabilitation Service

Participants	*Affiliation*
Dr. Paul Adams	J. Hillis Miller Health Center University of Florida Gainesville, Fla.
Dr. Paul Bonnici	Columbus State Hospital Columbus, Ohio
Dr. John A. Boston	500 West 15th Street Austin, Tex.
Dr. D. M. Bramwell	State Department of Health and Welfare Division of Mental Health Concord, N.H.
Dr. Houston Brummit	147 East 50th Street New York, N.Y.
Dr. Frank Gaines	319 Fincastle Building Louisville, Ky.
Dr. Miguel Gracia	Montana State Hospital Warm Springs, Mont.
Dr. Paul Graffagnino	609 Farmington Avenue Hartford, Conn.
Dr. Roy Grinker, Sr.	Michael Reese Hospital and Medical Center Chicago, Ill.
Dr. John Hampson	School of Medicine University of Washington Seattle, Wash.

Participants	*Affiliation*
Dr. B. E. Kenney	Pottawattamie County Mental Health Center Council Bluffs, Iowa
Dr. Richard A. Levy	Maine Medical Center Portland, Maine
Dr. Thayer Mackenzie	2431 K Street NW. Washington, D.C.
Dr. William Mackenzie	1224 Halliman Circle Lake Oswego, Oreg.
Dr. Paul McQuaid	83 Nutley Lane Dublin, Ireland
Dr. Eugene Mindel	Michael Reese Hospital and Medical Center Chicago, Ill.
Dr. Tarlton Morrow	The Menninger Clinic Topeka, Kans.
Dr. Peter Ostwald	San Francisco Medical Center University of California San Francisco, Calif.
Dr. Kenneth G. Paltrow	University of Oregon Medical School Portland, Oreg.
Dr. Joyce Perrin	1163 East Ocean Blvd. Long Beach, Calif.
Dr. Richard Pfrender	University Hospital University of Michigan Ann Arbor, Mich.
Dr. Robert Quirmbach	Department of Mental Hygiene Agnew State Hospital San Jose, Calif.
Dr. Luther Robinson	Saint Elizabeth's Hospital Washington, D.C.
Dr. William B. Rothney	Tufts-New England Medical Center Boston, Mass.

Participants	*Affiliation*
Dr. Irving Rothrock	Kansas University Medical Center Kansas City, Kans.
Dr. David Rothstein	55 East Washington Chicago, Ill.
Dr. Lindbergh Sata	The Psychiatric Institute University of Maryland Baltimore, Md.
Dr. Hilde Schlesinger	Langley Porter Institute San Francisco, Calif.
Dr. Edward Shipley	Marion County Child Guidance Clinic Indianapolis, Ind.
Dr. Felix Sommer	Brattleboro Retreat Brattleboro, Vt.
Dr. James A. Sonnega	Hawthorne Center Northville, Mich.
Dr. John H. Wolaver	2014 West Clinch Avenue Knoxville, Tenn.

Participating Staff of the New York State Program

Lawrence C. Kolb, M.D., Director, N.Y. State Psychiatric Institute
Alfred M. Stanley, M.D., Director, Rockland State Hospital

Syed Abdullah, M.D.
Kenneth Z. Altshuler, M.D.
Jean Badanes, M.A.
Steven Chough, M.S.W.
Tibor Farkas, M.D.

Adele Maurer, R.N.
John D. Rainer, M.D.
M. Bruce Sarlin, M.D.
Howard Tisk, M.A.
John Vollenweider, Ph. D.

Participating Staff of the New York School for the Deaf

Dr. Roy M. Stelle
Mrs. Mary Minor
Mr. Norman Jacoff

FOREWORD

Psychiatry and the Deaf is a unique contribution to the professional literature in an area in which knowledge and understanding are all too sparse. First, this work represents a pioneering step toward redressing the neglect which long has characterized psychiatric concern for the deaf. Second, the information within its pages is presented in a way that captures the vitality and spontaneity of spirited exchanges between knowledgeable professionals in the workshop of April 1967 at the New York State Psychiatric Institute.

Reading this report, with its free and informal style, can impart to one the feeling of joining in the same philosophical movement that motivated those who actually attended the workshop. Hopefully, the material presented here will be transformed into working knowledge useful in providing mental health services to persons who are deaf. Hopefully, too, the availability of this knowledge will stimulate new programs to bring better care to more of those who need it.

Of particular interest is discussion concerning the correction of misdiagnoses of hospitalized deaf persons and of the rehabilitation of the mentally ill deaf as exemplified by the State program in New York. Here is an encouraging and significant example of what can and must be done on a larger scale and in other areas.

It is deeply gratifying to me and to my associates in the Social and Rehabilitation Service that our agency had a part in this publication, and in the workshop which inspired it.

MARY E. SWITZER
Administrator
SOCIAL AND REHABILITATION SERVICE

IX

Editors' Preface

This monograph reports a meeting unique in medical history. For the first time psychiatrists from all parts of the country came together to learn about, to discuss, and to exchange views gained from their psychiatric and psychological work with the deaf. Supported by the Rehabilitation Services Administration (formerly the Vocational Rehabilitation Administration) of the Social and Rehabilitation Service, the meeting was cosponsored by the New York State Psychiatric Institute and the New York University Center for Research and Training in Deafness Rehabilitation. It was held at the New York School for the Deaf in White Plains, N.Y., the Rockland State Hospital in Orangeburg, N.Y., and the New York State Psychiatric Institute at Columbia University's Medical Center in New York City. All of these agencies had long cooperated with the Institute's Department of Medical Genetics as that Department pioneered in developing—and then gradually extended—its network of psychiatric services to the deaf.

Interchange was lively and enthusiasm high throughout the conference. Doctors who felt they had been working in the dark were excited to find others who shared their interest, and they were quick to take advantage of the chance to learn from each other, share their difficulties, and gain in experience.

In preparing the manuscript, we have tried to keep intact this feeling of excitement and discovery by reporting the meeting as it unfolded. The *first day* included visits to the New York School for the Deaf and to New York's unique inpatient unit for the deaf at Rockland State Hospital. At both places there were presentations of the psychiatric programs designed for the particular setting, presentations of special individual material, and plentiful discussion from the participants; all of this has been retained, from introductory remarks to questions and responses from the floor. The result reads more like a play than a text, and we hope that the reader will find it easier going than he would if the material were more bookish.

The *second day* (at the Psychiatric Institute) was given over to theoretical and organizational matters presented by the staff of New York's project for the deaf, and to various aspects of their own experience volunteered for discussion by the participants. Here too we have tried to hold to the informal feel and discursive sense of the original meeting. It is our belief that the most abstruse concepts of theory and practice can generally be expressed in terms understandable to all. To reclothe them, for publication, with formal professional jargon and a scholastic veneer would fail to convey the very spontaneity and basic sense of interest that was the heart of the conference; it would also limit the readership to dedicated scholars and self-punishing insomniacs. We will have reported this conference accurately only if you sense the vitality of the area and fleetingly wish you had been there.

We would like to acknowledge the assistance of Drs. Boyce Williams and L. Deno Reed of the SRS and the effective efforts of Drs. Edna Levine and McCay Vernon who formed, with us, the planning committee for the conference. Miss Mima Cataldo and Mr. Steven Johnson worked unstintingly in handling all administrative matters and arrangements, and Hella Freud Bernays assisted with the editorial task.

John D. Rainer, M.D.
Kenneth Z. Altshuler, M.D.

Editors

TABLE OF CONTENTS

Second Day—Continued

Background and History of
New York State Mental Health Program
for the Deaf

Dr. John D. Rainer

Dr. Rainer:

I want to welcome you to this genuinely historic conference devoted to a new psychiatric subspecialty, a conference which has been too long in developing. We are meeting this morning at the New York School for the Deaf in White Plains, N.Y. where we will be able to see the children, the school, and part of our program in action.

This is the first time, I believe, that a group anywhere approaching this size of psychiatrists specifically interested in the problem of psychiatry for the deaf has gotten together. I think of this workshop today as only the ground breaker, the first among many gatherings of our profession devoted to psychiatric concern with the deaf. Let me begin by telling you how my colleagues and I visualize these 2 days, what we hope will happen, and what our plans are. We want, above all, an interchange of experiences, of ideas, and of questions among all of us. The history of psychiatric concern for the deaf is a recent one, and we have much to learn from one another.

A little over 10 years ago, with Dr. Edna Levine and the late Dr. Franz Kallmann, we first set up a psychiatric research project and a clinical program for the deaf. At that time we were very much aware of the total lack of information about the deaf that existed on the part of psychiatrists and mental health agencies. We ourselves had been drawn to an interest in the deaf because of our experience in marriage, parenthood, and family counseling, and also because of our research on the etiologic and contributing factors in mental illness. With the exception of Dr. Levine, who had been working with the deaf for many years, we came to this field from the outside. We were surprised to find a complete absence of psychiatric facilities for diagnosis and treatment of the deaf. Indeed, the very size of the group of deaf persons in New York State was not known.

For over a century, of course, rehabilitation specialists and educators had been working with the deaf. They knew that early deafness creates

1

unique adjustment problems. Psychologists were already devising better ways of measuring intelligence, thinking, and maturity of the deaf, and were beginning to tackle the emotional and feeling aspects as well. But the pathway to an understanding of psychiatric symptoms and to the delineation and availability of treatment, as well as to psychiatric care on an individual or group basis, was blocked by formidable communication obstacles. Even at the time, though, it was difficult to see why an area so rich in theoretical and practical problems, involving a group so deserving and needy of psychiatric help, was so grossly neglected by our profession. I suspect that it was more than just neglect, that there were some more subtle anxieties among us that accounted for this lack.

Let me illustrate by a brief anecdote: When our first book came out, "Family and Mental Health Problems in a Deaf Population," the Library of Congress, in printing their usual index cards that are sent to libraries throughout the Nation, had listed the project as "Mental Health Project for the Death." They hastily corrected the misprint, of course, but somehow, I felt it was a meaningful slip. The soundless world of the deaf was equated, unconsciously, by many persons, with lifelessness, with impenetrability, and with hopelessness regarding vital human contacts.

In the retrospect of 10 or 12 years, this attitude, fortunately, seems quite remote. How different it has been for all of us who have ventured to explore this territory. In our very first visits to State hospital wards, moving from building to building in search of deaf patients (many of whom had been there for decades), it was inspiring to us as well as to the patients, that, with our newly-acquired skills of manual communication, elementary as they were at the time, we were able to see the awakened contact, the chance to talk and to listen, of persons who had not communicated with anyone in years.

All of those connected with our program, from psychiatrists to ward attendants, have experienced a fascination and have developed a dedication and a loyalty which I believe could not have been predicted in those days. Perhaps those feelings were engendered by the inherent interest of the work, perhaps by the challenge of doing the seemingly impossible, or by the gratification of success, or by some special emotional satisfaction we found in reaching the deaf. In any event, all of us who have worked with these patients became inspired by the feeling that we are part of a special group who are privileged to do the job. I think this feeling which we have noticed as new people joined our staff, is something which bodes well for the future of this work in any of the areas or the States or the regions where all of you are beginning to work with the deaf.

Among the participants here are some who have had considerable experience with the deaf, some who are now engaged in programs for the deaf, and others who have been called upon to consult or are connected with State mental hygiene or rehabilitation programs serving the deaf. In the course of these 2 days, then, we hope that you will get some idea of our own mental health program, which started as that research and pilot clinical program in 1955.

In the first phase of our work, we found out all we could about the adjustment problems, the family problems, the sexual problems, the vocational problems, of the deaf population. We gathered many statistics on them. We studied the genetics of their deafness. We reviewed the lives of deaf achievers, those who had achieved professional status despite their handicap. In the clinical area, we set up a pilot clinic in which we saw over 250 patients in those years. Finally, we surveyed the State hospitals and found there were almost 250 deaf patients among the 100,000 patients in our New York State mental hospitals. In the course of this work, we evolved some thoughts on psychiatric examination and psychiatric diagnosis, we developed some methods of psychotherapy, and we formulated the need for an inpatient psychiatric program for the deaf.

Many of these matters you will be hearing about tomorrow. This afternoon at Rockland State Hospital you will see the inpatient program, the second phase of our project which began in 1963, where we have a 30-bed ward to which deaf patients can be transferred from other hospitals or admitted directly from the community. You will have a chance to see the patients, the group therapy program, the occupational therapy program, and the entire ward arrangement. This inpatient service as well as the outpatient service are now established as an integral part of the New York State Department of Mental Hygiene, and may serve as a model so that you may learn from our successes and benefit from our mistakes in setting up similar programs on your own.

The third phase of our program, presently supported by the United States Vocational Rehabilitation Administration, has to do with extending the program in two directions, rehabilitation and prevention. Rehabilitation has to do with assisting patients in their efforts to live and work in the community during or after their formal treatment. Prevention deals with mental hygiene in the early years and brings us directly to the schools—that is the main reason we are here this morning.

The deaf child is probably more dependent on the school, and dependent at an earlier age, than the hearing one, and hence, especially for those of you who have not had too much contact with schools, we will begin our demonstration with the educational aspects. You will have a chance to observe the early cradle—if you will—of the development of the deaf child. Dr. Roy Stelle will tell you about the school setting, and then Dr. Altshuler will open a session on the preventive psychiatric programs at the school level.

Following this discussion, you will hear from a panel of deaf adults, discussing their own lives and concern with mental health and adjustment. After lunch here at the school, we will proceed to Rockland State Hospital, for a demonstration of the inpatient service. Tomorrow we meet at the Psychiatric Institute. There we will have more detailed presentations of theoretical, diagnostic, therapeutic, and the organizational aspects of work with the deaf.

Tomorrow, those of you who have expressed the wish to do so, will be called upon. Time is also allotted tomorrow for discussion, and this will probably be the most important part of the meeting. Perhaps others of you would also like a specific chunk of time—perhaps 5 to 10 minutes—to tell the rest of us a bit from the platform of what you are doing. We want all of you to participate, to ask questions, to add to the discussion, both in the formal group and informally during the day and evening. In that way we can have a genuine workshop and really plant a seed for the future.

Introduction to the School Program

Dr. Edna S. Levine

Dr. Levine:

When I first entered the field of deafness as a clinical psychologist, a number of years ago, my major responsibility was to hew clinical paths, both in service and research. At that time it was a peculiarly monodisciplinary field—for educators exclusively. Another major responsibility, therefore, was to recruit new disciplines. I think our major achievement was to recruit psychiatry, at that time in the person of Dr. Franz Kallmann, and now his staff, Dr. Rainer and Dr. Altshuler, who are continuing his pioneer work.

We have waited long for this meeting, and have anticipated much from it. We wish to express how very welcome you are in this field, and how much we hope you will stay in it.

For decades the school has been a major influence in the lives and development of deaf people. In looking back to the educational methods formerly used with the deaf, you would have seen each pupil as an individual more or less encased in his own little glass tomb. Perhaps only then you might begin to appreciate that today's children don't show what deafness is, nor the true implications of what being deaf means.

It is strange to see happy children, as you will here, behaving the way ordinary children do in regular schools, and yet to realize that these children are quite different from those that you see in regular schools. Nevertheless, they are different—and I think in the course of the discussion we will arrive at some of the implications of this difference.

Suppose we begin by concentrating on what deaf people are exposed to regarding personal, scholastic, and social development in the course of their school program. Here to tell us and show us is Dr. Roy M. Stelle, superintendent of the New York School for the Deaf.

History of New York School for the Deaf

Dr. Roy M. Stelle

Dr. Stelle:

First, I wish to welcome you all to New York, and especially to the New York School for the Deaf this morning.

The New York School for the Deaf, the second oldest school for the deaf in the United States, was chartered April 15, 1817, and opened classes the following year. The first classes were held in New York's City Hall. It was Rev. John Stanford, then chaplain of the Almshouse in New York, who saw the deaf children in lower Manhattan, felt the need, and realized that something should be done for them. He interested some influential people, including DeWitt Clinton, who later became governor. It was he who became the first president of our board of directors.

Since then, the school has had four different locations, having moved from the city hall to 23d Street and from there to 50th Street, where Saks Fifth Avenue is today. In 1856, it moved to the area where the Columbia-Presbyterian Hospital is today, and there it stayed until 1938. By that time, those buildings were pretty well worn out. The surroundings were becoming too much of a city for the school, and so it moved out here. And we have been here ever since.

The buildings were all built in 1938, with the exception of the pre-primary building, which was completed just 3 years ago, as was the gymnasium, including the swimming pool.

There are many exciting things that we are just getting started on here, one of which is our experimenting with cued speech with the children. You may not yet have heard of cued speech, but you will probably hear something about it today, and get a chance to talk about it.

We have arranged this morning so that you may get a quick, bird's-eye view of the school. We will return here at 11 o'clock for further discussion and the rest of this morning's sessions.

Tour of the School
and Demonstration of Educational Techniques
at Various Age Levels

The tour of the school included the preprimary division, the elementary school, and the high school. The preprimary division, housed in a separate building, provided the visitors with a bird's-eye view of the art class, regular instruction classes, and speech training. In the elementary school, regular grade instruction was seen. High school classes in English, geography, mathematics, social studies and chemistry were visited.

Dr. Rainer:

We will now resume our workshop. Up to now you have really seen half of the background of mental health, the school part of it. You have seen the regular functioning of the educational system. The other half is in the home.

We are here, though, in our capacity as psychiatrists, especially interested in emotional problems of which you may not have seen too many in the classrooms as you went around. Dr. Altshuler will now take over and describe to you the preventive psychiatry program which we have initiated here at the New York School for the Deaf.

The Psychiatric Preventive Programs in a School for the Deaf

Dr. Kenneth Z. Altshuler

Dr. Altshuler:

Let me begin by telling you something of how our preventive program came into being.

We all know, of course, that the neurotic disturbances that we see in character and adjustment in adults have their roots in early experience in the family grouping, and generally evolve within that grouping. Usually, the first time children become available to influences from without is when they enter school. That deaf children require the maximum use of this opportunity should be self-evident. They are in isolation; also, the confusion and distress of the parents, in the face of the handicap and the need for the children to mature in the presence of a severe limitation, have been well documented.

It is of interest in this connection that one of our earliest studies of deaf criminals and delinquents indicated that their behavior had been visibly disturbed early in the school years, and that there were many times at which it seemed that if some suitable kind of intervention had been available, their subsequent criminality may perhaps have been averted.

Our first experience in the outpatient clinic with a number of students who were referred from various schools, led us to try to explore a little the needs within the school. Dr. Stelle was good enough to let us come here to the New York School for the Deaf, and Dr. Rainer and I undertook a series of consultations during the school years 1963 through 1965.

During that time we saw about 40 students for individual evaluation; it was necessary to see almost all of them more than once. What we did was to try to outline a program of treatment or environmental modification for them, as indicated, and the school psychologist, Mrs. Mary Minor, together with the social worker, Mr. Norman Jacoff, Dr. Rainer, and myself, formed a kind of mental health team. Mrs. Minor and Mr. Jacoff would carry the recommendations into action, and keep tabs on what was being done, so that we were able to get some kind of followup without having to see the students every week.

11

Of the pupils referred during that period 16 represented behavior disorders, and 14 children what you might call incipient character problems. There were another three with mental deficiency, and four who were childhood schizophrenics. On the basis of our experience we firmly believe that at least eight of the children were enabled to remain in school only because of the intervention of the team.

The problems we saw were what you would expect in any group of school children. There were poor academic performance, disciplinary problems, temper tantrums, hyperactivity, stealing, and sexual misbehavior. But we found, also, that there was a very curious lack of what you might call camaraderie, the kind of group sense that you come upon so often in hearing kids and young adolescents. This is the spirit epitomized most clearly in youthful gangs. These deaf children seemed to be more separate from each other, less involved with each other's feelings, less together.

It also became clear that a number of the children knew some of the rules for living, but that the subtler nuances of the reasons for rules and mores were lost to them, because of their difficulty in understanding. Some of their qualities of personality resembled certain aspects of the behavior which we have also seen in deaf adults. We will be talking more about that tomorrow.

There was also a considerable interest, and a great deal of active experimentation, in sexual function, but there seemed to be an abysmal lack of any kind of codified knowledge about reproduction, and again, about the reasons for responsibility in this area.

During the second year we thought we might try an innovation and see several students at one time in a group, with the idea that we might use the group experience to help them begin to feel more about what was going on in the other person, and to explore the potential for interaction between them; in addition we hoped to define, and help with, any common problems, preoccupations, and concerns. We thought also that there might be some possible age- or sex-specific differences in the patterns of thinking that we could come upon.

A collection of boys between ages 10 and 12 with whom we started seemed virtually unable to form any kind of group. They all remained individuals, each one of them clamoring for the doctor's attention. They were entirely uninterested in each other. We tried them for four or five meetings, but as we had only a limited amount of time, we decided we would stop with this group and start with an older group instead.

We then began two older groupings of boys 13 to 16 and girls 13 to 15. The boys' group gradually developed some kind of group identity and mutual awareness. The change was definitely in response to the doctors' management of the group. I doubt that it would have developed spontaneously.

For example, at first they behaved very much as had the younger boys, quite uninterested in one another. If the doctor referred a question which one boy raised to one of the other boys, there would be an indifferent shrug or off-the-cuff response without any attempt to see what the other person meant or was concerned with. Slowly, however, this indifference yielded, when the doctor began to point out several areas that seemed to be of concern to all the members of the group.

One of these areas that was most striking was a preoccupation with violence and retaliation. These kids were all very nonverbal and read very little. While you would think they would ordinarily be quite uninformed, it was surprising to us, that when one Sunday a local paper carried a picture of a boy who had accidentally shot his younger brother, each of the six or seven boys in the group had paid attention to that picture and had insisted on some explanation from their own family of what had gone on.

This topic really sparked the first lively interchange within the group. Each boy seemed surprised to be made aware of how interested every other boy in the group had been in the same event. It began, I think, to develop in them more of a group sense.

Later on we noticed something else. One little boy in the group had transferred only recently to the school and was having a pretty rough time of it; he was being picked on and he was complaining about it. We asked one of the other boys there, who was bigger and huskier, what he thought about it, and he said he too had transferred the year before and he had been through that road himself. Now that he had been here for a year, it was much better.

And so we ultimately suggested that the older one could perhaps advise the younger one, and even in a way take over as a big brother or a helper. At this suggestion, they were both very surprised. It would never have occurred to them. From the suggestion there developed a rather close friendship, and, needless to say, the younger smaller boy, who was now well protected, found his going a little easier.

The girls' group, from the outset, was much more communicative. The girls seemed more aware of each other, and somewhat more capable than the boys' group in certain areas of abstract thinking. For example, the boundaries between borrowing and giving and stealing were less blurred among the girls than the boys. Although both groups were concerned with sexual exploration and its consequences, the girls seemed to show a more farsighted interest in defining their future roles as wives and mothers.

As a result of this experience, we incorporated into our present program, which began about a year ago, a design for the continuation of group work at the school. We chose adolescents to begin with, because of our finding that the younger boys were slower to come into a group form. We also hoped to be able to supply to the group what we thought was needed information about the rules and the roles of growing up, and to instill some sense of that mutual concern and responsibility. And we wanted to do this at a time when it could best be integrated by the youngsters.

You will hear more about this experience tomorrow, when Dr. Sarlin will discuss it, and will show, also, a television tape that we made of one of the group sessions.

We also held conferences with several of the teachers, reviewing the problems of each class, and with the cottage parents whose responsibility has traditionally outpaced their status within schools for the deaf. We are convinced that properly informed, conscientious cottage parents can be effective parent surrogates; they do have a great deal of responsibility for the children, and if they are helped to fulfill this responsibility they can become, in time, valuable psychotherapeutic assistants.

Finally, we undertook group meetings of parents. Here we took two different age groups of parents, that is, their age groups defined by the ages of their children. We took the group of parents who had younger children in the five-, six-, and seven-year range, and we took another group who had older children who were adolescent. As we began, we didn't know what we would find, but we thought this field was worth while exploring.

A number of interesting things came up; for example, when we were discussing how you handle the deaf child in the family if the family is going to go to a movie. The parents had quite a discussion about this. Does the mother of the family stay home alone with the deaf child and the father take the other two to the movie, or do you take all three together? And what do you do when the child becomes bored and disruptive? I think it is through this kind of discussion that one really gets a sense of what it is to have a deaf child in the family. A myriad of day-to-day crises come to light as the parents kept trying somehow to handle the rest of the family, and at the same time do the right thing by their deaf child. These groups were led by Dr. Sarlin, who is here and who will be happy, later on, to answer any questions about them.

We became aware that the parents have a rough road to travel. The parents of the younger children met our efforts with an enthusiasm which seemed born out of their own hunger and need for some kind of chance to discuss their problems and to get some support from the views of other parents, and perhaps also from whatever magic or vigorous nodding of the head we might supply. We found that the parents of older children had already come a considerable way on their own; they proved a bit more difficult to work with, because they had already developed ways of dealing with the children and the problem, and they also had a vested interest at this time in denying any problems of their own which may have limited their effectiveness as parents. As a result there is a greater tendency in this group to make more demands on the school and to blame the various agencies for whatever failings there may have been.

One finding that I think was really striking was the statement from a couple of parents that both they and the children go through a really agonizing reappraisal at the time of early adolescence. It is at this time, that the deafness becomes most clear as a handicap. It is the time at which socialization really begins, and suddenly it is not enough if the kids can play ball with the other kids on the block. Now the boy-girl interests come up, and their child is virtually excluded.

It is a time at which the deaf adolescent and the parents have really to come to grips with the limitations that are involved in the handicap, that is, they become aware that all the hopes and the promises that this child would have normal speech, that he or she would be able to get along on a par with any of the hearing children, are quite likely to be dashed. Such straits require a great deal of reworking of the parents' feelings of inadequacy, as well as rekindle hostilities toward the various agencies which seemed to promise earlier that education for the deaf child would solve everything.

The parents who brought this out said they had found the most solace through discussions with other parents who had been through it themselves; these others provided support for the fact that the parents had not been at fault, but that probably the difficulties were inherent in the condition.

As a result of these discussions, I think we may well mix the groups up a bit in the future, so that some of the older parents can come in and talk with the younger ones, and perhaps we can lay the groundwork for avoiding what would otherwise be an even more painful experience. Our hope is, also, that the work with the younger group of parents will make this transition period easier.

Dr. Rainer, Dr. Sarlin, and I will try now to answer any questions you may have.

Discussion

Question:

Do you give some genetic counseling in regard to future babies, and the possibility of more hearing deficit?

Dr. Altshuler:

That is one of the things we hoped to get to in the groups. I am not sure it has been dealt with yet.

Here is one of the interesting things we found in our first survey: We interviewed about 300 deaf people and their families, and one of the questions we asked was: Would you rather have, or have had, a hearing child or deaf children? Almost unanimously they said that they would rather have had hearing children. Occasionally someone who already had a deaf child would say, "We're happy to have a deaf child." But generally, where a choice was presented, they expressed an interest in having hearing children. Yet, when we asked them, for example, about the hearing status of their husband, whether he was congenitally deaf or had acquired deafness, and whether this made any difference in their choice of mate, or whether they thought it ought to make a difference, they indicated a total lack of any sense that this would have anything to do with the deafness of the children.

Obviously, this is something which has to be met. Dr. Withrow of Illinois tried to develop a curriculum in which he instructed the children in genetic principles and in principles of sexual reproduction. He was very fortunate, because he had a young couple who were teaching the class, and the wife got pregnant during the course of the year, so there was much the children could learn in quite a natural way.

We have increasingly had, in the outpatient clinic, people coming in with questions about whether they should marry someone who is deaf, and what about the likelihood of deafness in the children? Of course this depends on the particular type of deafness. This attitude of healthy questioning grows as more people become aware that such questions exist.

Dr. Rainer:

It is not easy to answer that question, because the genetics of deafness has not as yet been fully elucidated, although a great number of people are giving attention to it now.

Our program began under the direction of Dr. Franz Kallmann, who was a foremost geneticist. In that study, Dr. Diane Sank, a member of our staff, reported in a chapter in our first book,[1] that about half of deafness was altogether genetic, the other half being sporadic, probably acquired in early infancy. Of the genetic half, about three-quarters is recessive, the other one-quarter being dominant in transmission, sometimes part of some special syndrome such as Waardenburg's syndrome.

Even in those with recessive deafness there seemed to be maybe 30 or 40 different genes involved. You cannot even say to two people, both hereditarily deaf and with deaf siblings, that marrying each other will necessarily produce deaf children. Sometimes they do have one deaf child after the other; sometimes they don't.

Most deaf children, in fact, are born of the marriage of two hearing parents, who may but usually do not have any deafness in the family. About 10 percent of deaf children, however, do have deaf parents.

Until one really has a positive test for the particular gene involved, it isn't too easy to give definitive advice except that hereditarily deaf persons should not marry cousins. Nevertheless, at this stage of our scientific knowledge, probably one should be advised to try to avoid marriage between two persons with recessive hereditary form of deafness.

Dr. Altshuler:

There is even a problem in knowing precisely what the type of deafness is that the person has. When we inquired "How did you become deaf?" of 300 people, we very often met with the response that "I fell on my head," or "I fell off the table." You don't get deafness that way, any more than you get syphilis through the genes. When you ask further, "How do you know that?" they frequently say, "My mother told me." Here again, more and more questions begin to be raised as one is able to get individuals better educated to the fact that such problems exist.

[1] Rainer, J. D., Altshuler, K. Z., Kallmann, F. J. and Denning, W. E. (eds.) *Family and Mental Health Problems in a Deaf Population.* New York State Psychiatric Institute, 1963.

Question:

In your group work with the deaf, children and parents, did you do all the communicating yourselves, or did you have an intermediary in any way?

Dr. Altshuler:

We do the communicating ourselves. Dr. Sarlin has been running the groups of late. We have the assistance of Mrs. Minor and Mr. Jacoff, who are skilled also in manual language, so that if we miss something, they pick it up.

One of the things we are contemplating now is getting a television setup whereby we would have a chance to review what has gone on in the groups, to see whether what we think happened actually did happen, or whether something in addition happened that we may have missed. I think this would increase the correctness of our observations, and it would at least provide a check of them.

Question:

By working with the parents of 5- and 6-year-old deaf children have you been able to bring about any realization at all or a greater realization of the implications of deafness, so that these parents won't wait until their children are adolescent before they are aware of the real impact of deafness?

Dr. Altshuler:

We are trying to do that.

Dr. Sarlin:

In our efforts with the parents of the younger age group, we find that they talk a great deal about their feelings at having a deaf child, what it means to them. One of the points we try to get across to them is that deafness is a limitation, that all of us have limitations to some extent, and that it has got to be accepted. We also encourage them as best we can to communicate with their children by whatever means they have available. We have found that some, after many years of discouraging the use of the sign language, realize that perhaps there is value in learning it. Some of the parents have requested books on how to learn the language in order to be better able to communicate with their children. I think there have been some satisfying results from this as the children cease to be strangers and the handicap becomes less foreign.

Dr. Altshuler:

We have tried also to modify the parents' hopes. I think the way one does this is not with a sledge hammer, but gently, rather, over a period of time; for example, we indicate the statistics of the likelihood of clear speech developing, and from time to time bring out what the average level of function of these children is when they graduate from a school for the deaf. This can serve to stimulate discussion— that the level of function is not as high as it is among children who graduate from regular school. These things come out in a way that we hope will make that adolescent period easier on everybody.

Dr. Schlesinger:

In San Francisco one of the ways we found that might help that problem is to take ENT doctors who never meet any adult deaf to the special schools. All those I have taken there have decided to change their overoptimistic advice to parents of newly-discovered deaf youngsters. They had formerly given very unrealistic expectations and had helped to provide some of the distortions which the parents were only too glad to hook on to.

Dr. Rainer:

What we find is that in the beginning the parents start out with an overoptimistic picture, perhaps fostered by some poor advice they have gotten, and gradually, as the youngsters get into the difficult adolescent stage, they end up being overpessimistic. One has to try to even it off at both ends.

We have been pushing this program for practical reasons, only as far back as the parents of preschool children, but this isn't really far enough. We have to make it available to the parents of very young children just as soon as they find out their difference, at the age of a year or so. I believe some of you already have programs in which this is being done, in which somebody goes to visit parents of known deaf children at an extremely early age.

Dr. Rothstein:

Ours is called the Deaf Baby Program and is operated through the public school system. Attempts are made to put appropriate hearing aids on the children as soon as the diagnosis is made. There are now 20 such babies in the program, about 18 months of age, and the program also attempts to provide counseling and support for these parents. It has been in operation for only about a year, so I cannot report just how it is doing.

Dr. Mindel:

We have been at it for less than 1 year, so there is really not a great deal to talk about. We are working through the Hearing and Speech Clinic at Michael Reese Hospital, and see parents who come through there, also deaf children. Our interest there is in charting the dynamics of dealing with the disabled child, in the behavioral patterns, the play patterns, of this kind of child.

Dr. McQuaid:

We have a program in Dublin, Ireland, which is modelled on the English development of a register of high risk babies. Burt Sheridan has been successful in setting this up in our charity hospitals. We are trying to establish a list of children who may develop deafness. This is for early intervention. We think it is important to get at potentially deaf children just as early as possible.

Dr. Altshuler:

This is very good to hear.

Question:

One of the aims of the general program for the deaf is to prevent deafness and to control deafness as a genetic factor. Is this one of the aims of your program, to control deafness as a genetic factor?

Dr. Altshuler:

Those parents who come for advice are given the likelihood of results in their issue. In our discussions with them, we try to help them to decide, but we do not attempt to influence their choice of marriage partners. We believe that they are entitled to make their choice on the basis of as much information as possible and full awareness of what is likely to ensue.

Question:

Do you find many of the deaf youngsters being sent to schools for the mentally retarded? What facilities do you have in this area for the mentally retarded deaf child? I found this common in Boston: Many of the deaf children, because of the lack of information about schools for the deaf, had parents who tended to think of them as mentally retarded and so sent them to a school for the retarded for a number of years.

Dr. Levine:

It has happened here, but in our board of education schools for the deaf in New York City we do have classes for those who are termed mentally retarded. I always hesitate to designate them as such, because some of them are actually functionally retarded. We also have rather an unusual development in the board of education, where we have the multiply-handicapped or aphasic or language-disordered type of child. In Manhattan we have one school entirely for that type of child, and now other schools are being developed in the other boroughs of New York City for that type of child.

Dr. Brummit:

I am from the school you mentioned in Manhattan. We have quite a bit of difficulty trying to get a child into this school, which has over 600 pupils. What is the breakdown or source of the children you have in this institution? Since we have only poor parental response, I wonder how large is your parental group and what percentage of your parents are really active in your parental groups?

Dr. Altshuler:

Let me answer the last part of your question. Our parental groups are still experimental and because of time limitations we have only two so far. What we are trying to do is something that will be essentially of a demonstration character and that we hope can be expanded if there is any indication of real success.

Mr. Jacoff:

In this school we have 275 children, running the whole age range from the 3½-year-olds, all the way up through our junior-senior high school program., where we have youngsters approaching 19 and 19½. To come back to the selection of parents for these groups, it was our original idea to try to have both parents come to the meeting if possible; if a group meets during the daytime, you get mainly mothers; it is virtually impossible for fathers to come during daytime hours. That is why we planned evening meetings.

In our selection of parents, we deliberately invited those for both the younger and the older groups who we felt and knew would be interested enough to participate. To start the program we wanted to insure having people who were motivated and concerned about their children, who had the time, who would be able to get a babysitter, who would be free on Wednesday evenings, and so would be able to come here. In this sense the selection was not entirely a random one.

Dr. Brummit:

I am interested in the philosophy behind the selection of the children. Where are you getting the pupils from? Do they come primarily from New York City or from the local area?

Mr. Jacoff:

This school serves an area that includes New York City. Of the 275 children, 110 or 112 live in one of the five boroughs. The rest live either out on Long Island or in upper New York State, as far up as Albany. In the area we serve, we have about 83 or 85 day children in Westchester and Rockland Counties. These children do not live here but come each day by bus.

Question:

Are you working with any families where both parents are deaf?

Dr. Altshuler:

No, we have not done that yet. We hope in the fall to establish another group which will include parents who are themselves deaf.

Adjustment Problems of the Deaf: Panel of Deaf Adults

Mrs. Frances Friedman
Mr. Max Friedman
Mrs. Naomi Leeds
Mr. Alan Sussman

Dr. Levine:

It gives me particular pleasure at this time to introduce to you a panel of deaf adults. All of them are leaders in the field of the deaf, some in the community in general, and they will bring you their own observations, experiences, and thoughts. First let me introduce Mrs. Frances Friedman, who is associated with the Grolier Publishing Company.

Mrs. Friedman:

My name is Frances Friedman. Mine is the story of a hard-of-hearing person who has shunted among three worlds—the hearing world, the hard-of-hearing world, and the deaf world.

At the age of 18 months, through an accident, I lost the hearing completely in my left ear. For some unknown reason, 50 percent of the hearing in my right ear was affected, but it was not known until I reached the age of 6, when the teacher noticed that I was not responding when my back was turned to her. The doctors found that I was very hard of hearing, and advised my parents to send me to a school for the deaf. My parents took me to one in New Jersey, and as I did not get a very good impression of that school, they decided to let me go to regular schools, and see how things went.

I attended regular school until my third year in high school, when I found the going rather rough. I was advised to go to a school for the deaf in Rochester, N.Y. I went there for 1 year but found that they could not teach me any more lip reading than I already had. I had a natural aptitude for lip reading, which seemed to have come to me from the very beginning of my hearing loss. I went back to regular high school, graduated, went on to Cornell University, stayed for 1½ years as a special student for the liberal arts, and then transferred

to the University of Buffalo as a special student in library science.
I remained there for 1½ years, until illness in the family forced
me to leave. These 2 school years were hard ones, because in those
days teachers were not as understanding of a hearing-impaired person as they are today. Teachers had a bad habit of walking around
the back of the room and lecturing from there. If you turned your
head you were reprimanded. But somehow or other I managed to get
through that. Also, these were not happy years. I did not have much
of a social life. Children seemed to sort of—they would not exactly
shun me—but they were shy of me because they weren't sure how to
address me. In those days I did not have a hearing aid, so I depended
completely on lip reading, which was not too bad, but not enough to
give me the normal social life a child should have.

At the end of my course at University of Buffalo, I came to New
York City, job hunting. There I almost met my Waterloo. It was tough.
It didn't matter about my educational background. The answer was
always, "You are hard of hearing; I am sorry." Then I got wise; I
wouldn't admit I was hard of hearing until I got the interview over
with. But it was not easy to get a job in those days anyway, and even
harder for me. And so I started doing various things. I was a tea bag
inspector in a factory, the only deaf employee. Communication with
my boss was a little difficult because he was an Englishman. I found
it difficult to understand his accent, but somehow I managed. Next, I
got a job as an inspector in an underwear factory. You didn't need
any brains or speech or hearing, and so I got through that.

All the while I was working I was still looking. I covered every
agency for the handicapped that there was in New York City. But
at that time there were not too many. One was the New York State
Employment Service for the Handicapped. They were very understanding. They tried very hard, but jobs for people with my educational background were difficult to get. I tried addressing envelopes
by hand, typing envelopes—anything to keep myself busy and to earn
some money. At last I was called to the National Reemployment Service, and was given a job as a graphotype operator. It later became the
Unemployment Insurance Department, and I transferred to that
office.

In the meantime, I was making every effort to build a social life for
myself. I tried the hearing world. I was all right in a small group of,
say, three or four people where you could look around and communicate, but when it got to a larger number, I was lost.

Then I transferred to the hard-of-hearing group. That consists
mainly of people who really are deaf people but who consider themselves hard of hearing in that they are lipreaders. They do not use

the sign language, and they consider themselves quite capable of being understood when they speak. I was not happy there, either, because they had one characteristic that sort of repelled me, and that was their facial expressions. They had an ugly way of grimacing. It was very embarrassing to me. You must remember that I had just come from the hearing world, and so I was sort of repelled by this.

Then there was a very fortunate occurrence, for me. I was taken to a deaf gathering. It may seem strange, but somehow I felt that if I could learn their language, I would be more at home with them. I found through lip reading and following the signs that I was able to communicate with them. But it took a long time to read their responses. Eventually, however, I managed to get that, too.

At the Unemployment Insurance Office, I stayed for 5 years as assistant supervisor in the reproduction department. Then the agency moved to Albany, and I refused to move with them. And so I remained in New York, job hunting again. Despite my 5 years of experience it was still difficult. You see, people are afraid of the words "hard of hearing." I don't know what they imagined it would be, but they probably thought it wouldn't fit into their business world, and so I had another difficult time.

I married a deaf man, and for 20 years I was a housewife and a mother of two, a daughter and a son, both hearing. In our neighborhood, we were the only deaf couple, and we were a figure of speculation. People watched us and wondered how do we manage a normal life, how do we manage with the baby? But gradually, little by little, they learned to accept us.

When our daughter, who was the oldest, started to go to school, her problems started. The children would tell each other—and you know how cruel children can be—"Don't bother with her; her parents talk on their hands." She used to come home crying. But she was a brave little thing, and she solved her own problem. She brought the children to our home, and showed them that ours was the same kind of home as theirs, that she had the same toys and things they did, and that she did the same things they did. Gradually, their playmates came to our home and accepted us as they did their own parents, and too, they felt very flattered when they learned to spell and would say, "Hello," to my husband and me in the finger pattern. To this day, I still meet some of my daughter's schoolmates who spell "Hello," and are still very proud to remember it.

Our son is now 20 and in college. He never had the problem his older sister had. We had solved it before he was born, and so he had what you would call a normal life.

I then decided to go back to the hearing world, but this time with still another handicap, visually. My visual fields are very limited. I have partial vision in one eye and none at all in the other. With that I went back job hunting. For 1 full year I conscientiously covered every agency you can name. One agency for the blind said I had too much vision; somebody else said I had too much hearing; somebody else said I didn't have enough. Well, where was I going from there? I went to the Division of Vocational Rehabilitation, and for 1 year I was interviewed, tested, sent here, sent there—but still no job.

Finally, I asked if they could send me to JOB, a private agency that finds jobs for the almost impossible. They got me a job, but the employer said to me, "We have never hired a hearing- or a visual-handicapped person. We just don't know what to do with you. But the JOB people were very convincing. "We'll try you, but only at night when there is no one here. We'll try you for 2 weeks." Then he said to me, "How shall I speak to you?" I said, "Just the way you are talking to me now." This happened 8 years ago, but I still remember it vividly.

I worked there for 4 nights and was transferred to the day shift, where I stayed for 5 months. Business was very slow, however, and I was laid off. But I was immediately placed by JOB again, this time in my present job, with the Grolier Educational Corporation, publishers of the *Encyclopedia Americana*. I am now an order supervisor, with great responsibility. I handle the paper work for over $1 million a year of business, all by myself.

As regards our social life, I don't know what to say about whether it is good or not. I would say that mostly, now, I am with our deaf world. I say "our" advisedly, because I consider it mine, too. I am still not happy with the hard-of-hearing group. I am still irked by their attitude about their deafness. They will not admit that they are deaf, despite the fact that many of them have no hearing at all. I think I would have more respect for them if they would say, "We are deaf, but we prefer not to use the sign language." I believe in both methods, the combined and the oral group, but I would say on the whole my life has been a happy one, a good one.

Dr. Levine:

We shall hear next from Mr. Friedman, who is one of our outstanding deaf leaders on the national scale. In New York State he represents so many organizations that I will mention only one of them. He is editor of the *Empire State News*, which is the voice of the deaf of New York State. It gives me great pleasure to present Mr. Max Friedman.

Mr. Friedman:

Gentlemen, let me bid you welcome to a world you will no doubt find strange and to a people who badly need your services. When the Mental Health Project for the Literate Deaf was established in 1955, one of its objectives was to train psychiatrists to work with the deaf. While I never expected to see such psychiatrists turned out in assembly-line fashion, I—and others like me—did hope that a number of you could be recruited to work in our area. I do not have precise facts and figures. All I do know is that there is a very great shortage of psychiatrists who can work with the deaf. I know that this shortage of psychiatrists is universal, and that the deaf are not the only ones to suffer because of it. Nevertheless, we deaf number in the hundreds of thousands, and psychiatrists available to serve us can be numbered, possibly, on the fingers of my two hands.

This shortage can be explained. In many ways some of the deaf are peculiar, and their actions, thinking and responses are apt to be unlike those of any other group. You, gentlemen, have given years of your lives to learn about the ways of people with normal hearing. Who is to blame you if you do not wish to spend additional time learning the ways of this strange subculture? Furthermore, the communications problem is, to many of you, an insurmountable problem. But you are going to hear about that from others.

I should like to tell you of the organizations of and for the deaf. All of them, within their limited spheres, stand ready to be useful should you call on them for help or guidance, as you approach or attempt to work in this difficult field.

The deaf are great ones for joining. I, myself, can tick off 13 organizations to which I pay dues; if I were a teacher, an oralist, or a bowler, there would be several more. Some organization seems to exist to serve every purpose you can think of. One person who has taken the trouble to make a count tells me that there are 57 clubs or groups for the deaf in New York City. You may well ask why so many. The simplest explanation is that the deaf prefer their own company. Say what you will about integrating, many of us do, but when you come right down to it we are more at ease and more relaxed when we are in the company of those with whom we can converse without strain. And I can say categorically that in my experience those few I have met, who grew up with the deaf and yet prefer not to mix with them, are the oddballs.

I will pass over the card and the movie groups, the golfing, bowling and such athletic clubs, and the purely social clubs, since, though even these stand ready to render service, they do not properly belong in this paper. The Jewish and most Christian denominations have deaf congregations wherever they are enough people to form them. Most of them have clergymen to lead them, and it has been my experience that the clergymen and lay leaders are most useful when help of any kind is needed.

The largest organization of the deaf in the world—and I am including Soviet Russia, where their national groups are led and supported by the government and therefore are not *of* the deaf but *for* the deaf—is the National Fraternal Society of the Deaf. We have about 12,000 adult members and a treasury in excess of $5½ million. This is an insurance fraternity which also pays sickness and accident benefits, and it is run from top to bottom by the deaf. Here, if I may, I would like to digress a bit. I have something that will interest you as medical men. The mortality rate of members of the NFSD is better than the average of the 25 largest insurance companies in this country. So it appears that we deaf, in spite of all our shortcomings, are pretty healthy specimens.

Another large national organization is the National Association of the Deaf, with several thousand members. It is a confederation of state associations for the deaf. In New York the Empire State Association of the Deaf, which itself has seven branches, is an affiliate of the NAD. The NAD concerns itself with advancing the welfare of the deaf and in being our spokesman in such areas as employment, education, civil service, social welfare, and the like. Right now it is active in a legal case in California where a deaf couple was refused the right to adopt a child. The NAD is also a clearinghouse for information on the deaf, and if they themselves do not have the information you may seek they tell you where you can get it.

The Gallaudet College Alumni Association has many chapters throughout this country. You can always find some people in each chapter whom you can call on for help when it is needed.

There are also the schools for the deaf to which you can turn. It seems to be the most natural thing to do to turn to one of these schools, and I can recommend them, but with a reservation. I have been hearing complaints lately that whenever a deaf person is in trouble the first ones the authorities turn to are the schools. This makes many of us feel that the deaf are still tied to the schools' apron strings.

Not long ago, the Registry of Interpreters for the Deaf was formed. As the name indicates, these are people who are familiar with our language of signs. Most of the members are teachers of the deaf or of children of deaf parents. They are available where interpreters are needed, and it stands to reason that they can be useful in other ways, too.

There is another group that merits mention because you are all doctors of medicine. This is the Deafness Research Foundation which supports research on the causes and cure of deafness. Otologists among you might be especially interested in their work.

Lately new centers for the deaf have been sprouting up, notably in Wichita, Kansas City, St. Louis, Boston, Schenectady, and Dallas. All of these centers have trained and experienced deaf people on their staffs. We can expect more such facilities to come into being as the general public becomes more aware of the needs of the deaf. Thanks to federal grants, many young deaf college graduates are taking courses to train themselves in such fields as psychology, vocational rehabilitation, and social work. So, while we deaf do not have enough psychiatrists to meet our needs, genuine if slow progress is being made in other rehabilitative fields.

Dr. Levine:

We shall hear next from Mrs. Naomi Leeds, who is president of the Mental Health Association of the Deaf, Inc.

Mrs. Leeds (Interpreted by Rev. Louis Jasper):

The Mental Health Association of the Deaf was founded 3 years ago, by a group of deaf people in New York working as a volunteer organization with psychiatrists, and incorporated last year. At present there are 15 members, and every year we add more people to our organization. The members pay their dues not with money but with their hearts and their hands.

Ours is a service organization, dedicated to serve the deaf mentally ill patients in the metropolitan area who are forgotten by the public, often by their families, and by the deaf as well. Our other aims include bringing about understanding among the deaf as to the needs and the problems of the deaf mentally ill, to bring the deaf community and the mental health services together, to pass on information about the various aspects of mental health as it affects us, the deaf, in our day-to-day living, through literature and public programs such as we gave last December in New York City. That program included talks by mental health authorities and a play by the deaf on the return of a psychiatric patient to the community.

Our group came into being 3 years ago, triggered by a chance item in a local news column of my hometown paper, which read, "Would anyone be interested in donating art supplies to a deaf mute who taught himself to draw, an inmate in the nearby state hospital?" I showed the item to my friend, Mrs. Hlibok, who happened to drop in, and together we decided to do what was suggested.

First, we visited the hospital, and this was an eye opener. The patient, a man in his fifties, who looked 70, was a pathetic figure, poorly dressed and obviously neglected. He told us in halting sign language that we were his first visitors in 12 years! He described the same, deadly, daily routine of his life, and how he remembered his father's last visit, many years ago, and that he had not heard since from his deaf brother.

He told how he decided to teach himself to draw, and by picking up discarded newspapers and through the kindness of some nurses who gave him some drawing paper, pen and ink, he had learned to copy paintings in his spare time. In such simple pictures, he described his loneliness and emphasized how happy he was because of our visit. We went home disturbed, and determined to help him and others like him.

Mrs. Lee Brody, Mrs. Albert Berke, Mrs. Fay Cohen, together with Mrs. Hlibok and myself, formed the nucleus which finally led to the establishment of our organization, our incorporation in 1966, and to the growth of awareness and interest in our work on the part of the deaf public, through active membership and programs.

We are an independent organization, and we are encouraged and supported in our work by the deaf community at large. For example, in our yearly appeal for donations, for Hannukah-Christmas gifts for deaf patients, we have been given generous cash donations by clubs and organizations of the deaf, such as the Merry-Go-Rounders, an oral club, the Hebrew Association for the Deaf and its Sisterhood, the Women's Club of the Deaf, Inc., and from the Lutheran deaf group, the Long Island Catholic Deaf Association, and the Sisterhood of Beth Or of the Deaf, Inc., the Brooklyn Association of the Deaf, Inc., as well as many personal donations from the deaf public.

And in still other ways, when we ask for help in connection with our program, outside of our volunteer members, they answer our appeal and give of themselves unstintingly, often at great sacrifice to their free time and to their families, but without any thought of reward except to make our programs the success they have been, due to their group and individual efforts.

Our volunteer members, besides helping out with our programs, also make our deaf patients happy by their visits. They give special parties on holidays, provide clothing and gifts as well as refreshments. They pave the way for others to be understanding of patients who have been released, by treating them no different from others, and welcoming and accepting them at clubs and at their homes.

There is still another part of our organization, without which we would not be complete. They are our honored hearing advisory board, members who are prominent in their respective fields, or in connection with the deaf. They gave us the impetus needed to make our organization grow toward the achievement of our goals.

Dr. Levine:

We shall next hear from Mr. Alan Sussman, who is the only deaf counselor in the Division of Vocational Rehabilitation in the State of New York, besides being a candidate for a doctoral degree at New York University.

Mr. Sussman:

My topic, vocational adjustment of the deaf, problems and achievements, is a most appropriate one for me as a vocational rehabilitation counselor. It is likewise appropriate for this audience, because it has strong mental health overtones involving, as it does, personal adjustment.

A statistical breakdown of the employment picture of the deaf is obviously beyond the scope of this short talk, but this I will state emphatically: The problem is not unemployment, for the deaf are a highly employable group. The problem is, rather, underemployment. The deaf, as a whole, are a patient lot, although there are many in stereotyped occupations far below their true capabilities. In other words, from the point of view of employment, they are not operating at or near their level of potential.

Whenever we say a deaf person has a job, we should always ask these questions: Is he truly vocationally adjusted? Is he functioning in a job commensurate with his ability? Is he happy in his job? He may indeed have a job, but he may not be psychologically and aptitudinally attuned to it, with the result that there is job dissatisfaction and general discontent.

We all know that work is an essential part of a person's life, and that job dissatisfaction or vocational maladjustment creates serious mental health problems.

In my opinion, it is rare for a deaf person to be in a job that is ideally suited for him or her. It would be belaboring the point to state that deafness with its concomitant problems of communication difficulties, of poor language, low educational achievements, is responsible for this groupwide devaluation from the norm in terms of occupational distribution.

For example, only about 1 percent of the total deaf population is to be found in the professional classifications. And it is lack of guidance that contributes to this disparity. Proper vocational guidance, especially if it is geared to the deaf, would help the deaf person to avoid the pitfalls that lead to vocational maladjustment. For this and other obvious reasons, the deaf need more attentive and intensive vocational guidance than do the hearing.

In an effort to emphasize what I have already said let me focus on a certain occupational group of deaf people, the well-paid printers. As many of you know, there are a great many deaf people in the printing trade. These people are often called the aristocrats of the deaf community.

This group is relatively well educated, intelligent, and quite a number of them are talented college graduates. It is mainly from this occupational group that the deaf community draws its leaders. However, I believe that they have been pigeonholed into this occupation and that, as printers, they are functioning woefully below their potential.

Many of these printers are aware that they are cut out for more challenging occupations, and they make no bones about blaming their present occupational status on the guidance they should have had but never got. Nonetheless, we do not find them moping about their status. They compensate by assuming the leadership role and being active within the deaf community. Perhaps that explains why we have so many deaf leaders among the deaf.

This type of avocation—and I use avocation advisedly—provides them with an outlet through which they can exercise their abilities, which otherwise would have very little outlet. Their trade prevents them from functioning at their potential in the occupational world, but they are relating to the deaf world, and this they find rewarding. You may call it sublimation, if you will; they adopt a defense mechanism, and become problem oriented, not ego oriented. This helps to maintain and enhance their mental health.

But what about others who do not have the ability, the know-how, or the style to cope with problems which stem from job dissatisfactions? I believe this group is becoming a bigger problem every day.

Let us shift the scene to a brighter horizon, the deaf professional people. They comprise, as I have already remarked, a very small group. They exemplify one way of overcoming the serious disability of deafness.

The professional group includes scientists, engineers, psychologists, guidance counselors, dentists, and so forth. Some have managed to

circumvent the old bugaboo, the telephone, by having personal secre-
taries of their own, or have become so valuable to their employers that
their handicap was accepted. An impression prevails that the deaf
professionals have made it big, and that they do not need as much help,
if any, as the average deaf people do.

Nothing could be further from the truth. The deaf professional
person may have made the grade occupationwise, but he may still not
have effected a total personal adjustment. The deaf professionals have
psychological problems of their own, as a direct outgrowth of their
rough climb up the educational and the professional ladders. Their
college experience has been extremely stressful and there are still
difficulties. They have gone through professional training that has
also been difficult, especially at the graduate level. As professionals
who have arrived they continue to be exposed to even more frustrating
and stressful situations.

This is a group of deaf people who are highly vulnerable to emotional problems. They are high achievers, but they are paying a very
high price to be what they are, and where they are. In other words,
high or low, there are problems that go beyond mere vocational adjustment, problems involving total personal adjustment.

It is a fact that the vocational rehabilitation of the deaf has come
a long way and that it is making rapid strides towards vocational adjustment of the deaf. Too much emphasis, however, is being placed
on job placement. More emphasis should be placed on the conduct of
the whole man, on the total personal adjustment of the deaf individual.

The deaf are in need of help along these lines: adjustment, adjustment to deafness, personal family counseling. We also need vocational
guidance at the adult level, and vocational and personal guidance
while on the job, not only in preparation for it.

There is, for the deaf as for others, the problem of adjustment to
ever-increasing leisure time. Many deaf people do not know what to
do with so much time on their hands. There is the problem of adjustment to old age, and adjustment to the deaf, as well as to the hearing
community. For the deaf there is a great need in the area of preventive
psychiatry, or just plain mental hygiene.

Dr. Levine:

Summing up, I think that what each of the speakers has given you
is something of his own method of compensating for what he experiences in being a handicapped person. In that respect we might say
that each of the speakers imparted to you some autobiographical information, expressed or not.

Mr. Sussman, for example, had a great many years of experience as a printer before he decided he had had it, and decided to go back to school. Now he personally is experiencing what the problems of the deaf professional person are. This is a group we are just now beginning to explore. In discussing their experiences and ideas with you, the panel has really expressed how the deaf view their problems. I think we must admit that a great many of their problems are also our problems. It becomes our responsibility to devise the means for doing a more effective job in solving their problems.

The Psychiatric Inpatient Program

Tour of Facilities

The afternoon session was held at Rockland State Hospital at the Special Unit for the Deaf. This unit is a permanent part of the facilities of the New York State Department of Mental Hygiene and is the only one of its kind in the world. It houses 30 adult patients, 15 of each sex, and provides such ancillary services as occupational therapy, social service casework, psychological services, rehabilitation counseling and educational services, in addition to its basic mission of intensive psychiatric treatment of the deaf. The staff are all skilled in manual language so that from nurses' aides to physicians, all can communicate with the patient to whatever extent he is able.

A recent addition to the unit's program is a kind of "intramural industry." This consists of the manual assembly by patients of various items that are sent in for this purpose by industry and returned for commercial sale when the assembly is completed. Patients performing this kind of work earn a modest remuneration in accord with the number of items assembled, and at the same time their performance is viewed and rated to assist the rehabilitation counselor in determining vocational feasibility, concentration span, dexterity, and the like. During the course of the afternoon session the group of psychiatrists was able to observe this workshop in operation as they toured the ward. In addition, they had the opportunity to see group psychotherapy demonstrated with the patients of the ward. The group was run by Dr. Abdullah and demonstrated how even psychotic deaf patients can be brought into an active interchange and closer awareness of each others' personality problems and symptomatology.

The rest of the afternoon's program consisted of the demonstration of individual cases of various types of illness commonly encountered. Chairman of this session was Dr. Altshuler and the presentations were made by Dr. Abdullah, with opportunity for the audience (participating psychiatrists) to interview the patients from the floor, and for questions to be answered by the entire staff of the unit. It is with this part of the program that this volume continues, inasmuch as the tour, by its nature, could not be recorded.

Case Presentations and Discussion

Dr. Altshuler:

The first case we will show you is one that we have designated as a primitive personality. Dr. Abdullah will present the history.

Dr. Abdullah:

K.O., the girl whom we are going to see now, is interesting in many ways. When she came to our ward here, she was about 20 years old and she had lived a life of peculiar symbiosis with her mother. She never went to any school for the deaf; she was never exposed to any other deaf person and she went only briefly to a hearing school. She never understood anything, and was totally dependent on her mother for all her perceptual needs and expressions. She spoke to her mother and understood things through her mother, and lived a life wholly dependent on her mother. The mother always interpreted what her daughter said. Actually the mother interpreted what she herself felt rather than what the daughter felt.

The patient was a very much wanted child, born after 11 years of marriage. The mother was psychotic and had had a postpartum psychotic episode. The father was also borderline. When the patient was born she had some neck injury, and there was a hematoma on the neck. The doctor immediately pointed this out and emphasized the need for treatment, but the parents refused, immediately took over and said they know how to place pillows under the neck to correct the deformity, and absolutely refused treatment for the child. Their denial started from there. Even now the patient has this torticollis.

Soon after that, the pediatrician pointed out that the child was deaf, but both parents denied this. They said, "We talk to her and she answers," and they insisted that she go to a hearing school.

The school reported that the child was deaf and would have to go to a special school. The school sent a social worker to the parents' house, and the parents chased the social worker out, saying, "You are just not doing your job. The child is perfectly all right. We talk to her." That was the pattern.

The mother talked to the daughter and always got back from her answers that nobody but the mother understood. It was an extreme case of total denial of the situation. The girl stayed in this school for a while, going from one class to another without picking up anything, without doing anything. Soon she stopped going altogether. She never went out on her own either, for the mother always chaperoned her. All of this went on until the age of 14, when her father died. Then the mother hovered over her even more and took her even more under her shelter.

For the next 5 years the pattern became more extreme. The two were hardly ever seen out of the house. They had their own house and they lived inside it, and the mother alone would just go out for what she needed. The mother was developing her own paranoid delusions, and 5 years after the father's death she broke out in an acute psychotic episode. The neighbors found her crying, delusional, and hallucinating. They called the police and sent her to a state hospital.

But now this girl had nowhere to go. She clung onto the mother because she had just had no separate existence. She, too, was taken to the same state hospital and from there she was admitted here in July 1963, when this ward was opened. When she came she was a very frightened and extremely passive child. She cried all the time. She had no communication; she did not know how to relate to anybody. She was in a mess. The mother, of course, over there, cried too. She is still in a state hospital.

The program of treatment began with teaching her how to communicate and mingle with other people. She proved to be a very intelligent girl. Once given the training, she started picking up sign language, English, arithmetic, as well as other subjects. But still her passivity and fear continued. She wouldn't go outside on the grounds to the swimming pool. She was too frightened. She wouldn't do this, she wouldn't do that. But once given support, and if somebody went with her and with continuous encouragement, she gradually started coming and going out.

Next we started on the very major project of sending her to New York City to Fountain House.[1] You may have heard about the project. This, again, was a very novel experience for her. We managed to encourage her, and she went with a group of patients. Now she has come a long way and is able to communicate very well, telling the story of her life to the group.

---

[1] Fountain House is a nonprofit organization to assist persons who have undergone psychiatric hospitalization to make a successful readjustment to community living. In a day program centered in a new building, and in transitional employment projects, the first steps toward vocational rehabilitation are begun. In addition, Fountain House leases a number of small apartments where former patients may develop their capacity for independent living. A number of deaf patients have been integrated into these programs as part of our pilot project.

As she got into the group, her personality developed. At first she was absolutely silent. She would just sit in the corner and refuse to talk to anybody. Now she makes the group her audience, and can start talking; she can even monopolize the group. She has been going to Fountain House with some of our other patients for about 9 months now, and feels confident that she is now able to go to New York City on her own.

In group therapy today she said something quite significant. She was with a new boy who has just started to go to Fountain House (yesterday was his first day), and she was trying her best to teach him how to get to New York, but he is so slow in understanding. In the group she expressed her feelings about his slowness. In the beginning, she was in a worse position than he, but today she has developed a lot of confidence, and she spoke up very well, for her. It was a tranquil speech of hers to the effect that now she has outdone him.

Actually, she has been telling me for the last few days that now she can go to Fountain House on her own, it's not necessary for her to be accompanied any longer. She even brings in arguments: What will happen if the other one gets a cold? What will happen? She is not going to miss Fountain House. She will go on her own.

We will present her to you for a few minutes. We still don't know what her eventual placement will be. Her mother is still in the state hospital, and still very insensitive to the real needs of her daughter. When we have visited her several times in the state hospital, the only thing she asks us is, "Have you taught my daughter lip reading and speech?"

[Patient was presented.]

Dr. Abdullah:

Do you want to ask anything of the patient? She is a very nice girl, very warm. She has developed, has come out with her hidden endowments. She is much more confident, though still a little nervous. She still needs support. Do you want to say anything, or do you want to ask anything?

Question to Patient:

Do you enjoy going to town by yourself?

Dr. Abdullah:

She has never been that far.

Question to Patient:

Do you plan for a job in the outside world?

Patient:

Yes.

Question to Dr. Abdullah:

What is the extent of her hearing loss?

Dr. Abdullah:

She is totally deaf. A hearing aid is of no help. When she wears a hearing aid, she gets vibration only. Perhaps very early, if she had been treated along the lines of a deaf child, if she had had some residual hearing that could have been developed, it might have been different. But in her case the parental denial was so firm that she was never given anything. She was never even really tested for her deafness until late in childhood. However, the mother still insists, "She understands me, understands everything that I say."

Actually, the mother lives whatever life she has through her daughter. She regards her as practically a continuation of her own body.

Question to Patient:

What do you do at Fountain House?

Patient:

I don't know. I do different things. Clean blackboards and windows.

Dr. Abdullah:

Suppose we ask what she thinks about her mother. You don't remember? But you write her letters?

Patient:

It is a long time.

Dr. Abdullah:

She visited you here once.

Patient:

I don't know when I will go home.

Dr. Abdullah:

Why did you never go to a deaf school?

Patient:

Never. I went to a hearing school.

Dr. Abdullah:

Why? Did you have friends in school?

Patient:

I had friends that went to school but could never understand.

Dr. Altshuler:

We labeled this girl a primitive personality because it took us some time to know what lay behind the impenetrable barrier that we saw at first, and also because she seemed to maintain a kind of pleasant sociability despite the fact of her extremely disturbed background.

Here is our next case. This boy was also a diagnostic puzzler. We finally arrived at the conclusion that he was a primary behavior disorder. He is of interest, also, because at first he had no communication except in a kind of primitive pantomime. And because of his strange body build we thought there might be some genetic problems.

Dr. Abdullah:

This boy, Q.E., had a very unhappy childhood, besides the fact of his deafness, because his mother immediately rejected him. Within a year and a half he was living in foster homes, at times with his grandparents. He had very disturbed conditions in these foster homes. In one there were only women, and he learned as a little child to dress up like a girl. Perhaps the foster parents dressed him up like that; at all events, he still retains some of these remnants, he still likes to wear feminine clothes.

He had a total of about two and a half years of schooling in a school for the deaf, but always with an extremely disturbed situation in the home, and with constant changes of foster parents.

One of the best foster parents he had, with whom he developed ties, died, and that was another difficulty. Then he was changed to still another place. Once in a while the grandmother would take him to live with her. He never had a stable home situation, never lived in any one place for any length of time. He used to get into temper tantrums, when he would throw things. Nothing very serious happened, but it would become difficult for his foster parents to handle him at home.

When he had too many problems in school, at the age of 9, he was sent to Bellevue Hospital. There they kept him for 2 months. Then they thought that he didn't belong in the hospital and they sent him back. Very soon after, he was again admitted. From the age of 9, with but short intermissions, he was in state hospitals. The result has been that he developed in a very isolated way, and didn't get an opportunity to meet other deaf children.

He stayed in one mental hospital from 1956 until the time we got him in 1964, a long stretch of time, with no association established with anybody, and no friendships, because of his deafness.

When he came here he was a very angry young boy, with very poor communication, naturally with very little schooling and very little contact with the deaf.

We were very interested in and curious about him. We did all kinds of investigations on him—hormonal studies and body-type studies and chromosomal studies, to find out whatever we could. He had developed what we might call a language of the body. He talked in pantomime, but now he can express himself very well without carrying out any of this. We tried to place him back with his grandmother last year, but the arrangement failed. After a short while, she threw him back.

In the group today he said a most interesting thing, and I would like to come back to it tomorrow, if I get a chance. He said that his mother does not like him and she has always hated him. He said she beats him, and to this rejection by his mother he reacts in a normal neurotic pattern by using a five-letter word about her to express his hostility. What he is confused about, however, is the role of his grandmother, a confusion which he illustrated in the group by telling, "My grandmother loves me because she cried when she brought me back to the hospital." This he goes on repeating. His understanding is very limited. He is unable to understand that there can be guilt in a person at the same time that there is hostility and rejection. He repeatedly asked me, "If my grandmother doesn't love me, why did she cry when she brought me back?"

He has also said in the group, and he is quite confused about it, that he blames the doctors for somehow conspiring with his grandmother. A few months before, his grandmother had again brought him back. He had gone to her with great hope, and while there had been no behavior problem, she just said that the financial burden was too much for her and she couldn't keep him.

[Patient was presented.]

Dr. Abdullah:

Would you like to ask him anything?

Question to Dr. Abdullah:

I would like to ask him when he wants something, say a glass of water, how does he ask for it?

Dr. Abdullah:

Those things he picked up. A thing like that is very easy to show. Tell me, what happened when you went home last time with your grandmother?

Patient:

1966.

Dr. Abdullah:

He forgets the month. Any trouble?

Patient:

No.

Dr. Abdullah:

Then why did grandmother bring you back here? He didn't get a job so his grandmother couldn't keep him. He blames us. We kept postponing getting him a job so grandmother couldn't keep him and brought him back.

A problem he had was that he used to use makeup and cosmetics. He says that was before and now he has stopped. He used to wear a corset and all that, but he has got over that. He cannot spell very well (interpreting). He was transferred from the hospital, "not my fault," he says. They taught him to use lipstick, and all.

Question, to Dr. Abdullah:

What I was wondering about is, when he wants something, does he ask for it in a way which would estrange someone from him, or does he do it in a pleasant way?

Dr. Abdullah:

When his relatives used to visit him here, he used to have a pattern in which he would just ask for things—money, money, money—and if they gave him $1, he would be angry and throw it away.

We actually trained him to be nice to his relatives when they came because then they will visit him again. We tried to relate their reluctance to visit him and his tremendous pressure to "Give me, give me." Distant relatives would come, but he would not differentiate them from those from whom he could ask more.

We tried to interpret to the family that this is his way of wanting to be reassured. He does not know limits. He is merely emphasizing a point. But it looks to them as though he is about to attack them. This is his difficulty with so little language; he acts out everything. At times he looks very threatening. Unless you can explain this to the person who is going to handle him, there can be quite a problem.

But we have literally trained him how to smile and ask; how to be soft and gentle, because hearing people can easily get afraid and upset. This thing we have found over a period of time in group sessions. We tell him, "You used to say this sort of thing, but you have changed." There was so much movement and commotion that people would get upset about it.

Question to Dr. Abdullah:

I want to know if he has any fears.

Dr. Abdullah:

Do you feel afraid?

Patient:

Yes.

Dr. Abdullah:

Of what?

Patient:

Crowds of people, better at home.

Dr. Abdullah:

His understanding is very poor. He still thinks if just the doctors would pick up the phone and tell his grandmother, she would come and take him home.

Question to Dr. Abdullah:

Can you inquire about his erotic interests? Has he ever been interested in girls?

Dr. Abdullah:

We never found him in any kind of overt homosexual or heterosexual situation. He is a transvestite and effeminate, but he has never flaunted his effeminacy or been seductive. We have tried to keep a watch on him because of his nature, the way he walks and all that. One would say that he has changed a lot. He used to use heavy makeup. That was another thing we had to raise and discuss in the group, how feminine he looks and acts. He has developed some understanding, but it is not complete. He still sometimes uses cosmetics. He says, "God made me like that." That much he can say, and he does say it sometimes, but he is ridiculed.

Once in while, when his things are checked a corset that he bought turns up. He also uses perfumes at times.

Dr. Vollenweider:

I tested the boy's intelligence and gave him a Rorschach and figure drawings. One of the interesting things about him is that even though his behavior and interests are feminine, and he likes to wear the clothes and the makeup, he doesn't basically seem to be strongly identified with any sex role. There is a basic weakness of any kind of identification, which was another thing that goes along with the picture of the primary disorder of character.

Question to Dr. Abdullah:

Does he have an English-speaking background? Is the mother English speaking?

Dr. Abdullah:

His family constellation is as follows: His mother was born in the British West Indies. His father was an Italian. He was born out of wedlock. The maternal grandfather was of Spanish and Jewish origin. His maternal grandmother was of Negro, French, and Indian origin, and she tells me that she also had a little Roumanian and Hungarian blood.

Question to Dr. Abdullah:

The reason I am asking is because he has a communication difficulty, and I thought maybe his family might have contributed.

Dr. Abdullah:

They all speak English.

Question to Dr. Abdullah:

Did he originally think he was a girl?

Dr. Abdullah:

No. When he was very little and in one foster home, there were only girls and a mother, no father. He grew up there and the femininity seemed almost to be imprinted somehow. In his very early history records, we found that when he was 7, he had learned to dress up like a girl. Perhaps he was taught to dress up that way and he persisted in it.

Question:

Has he ever referred to himself as a girl?

Dr. Abdullah:

There is a certain inconsistency. In group therapy several patients jeered at him for his effeminate behavior. I then asked him if he was a boy or a girl, and he did not answer my question. But later he insisted that he was a girl, which caused other patients to laugh quite a bit. But he does not always give the same answer. He must have been joking. He has a good sense of humor. He can be very warm and affectionate. He can also be very angry, at times.

Let me ask him if he plans to get married. Do you plan to get married? The answer is "a little bit." He doesn't want a baby. Babies are too much trouble.

He says now that he does not like crowds and people here. He would be better at home where it is quiet, not with so many people around. He is a little uncomfortable. He doesn't like crowds. I asked him why. He says, "I'm afraid. I'm not sick. I can't hear what people say."

Dr. Altshuler:

Thank you. I think you can also sense in him the energy under the surface and the potential violence that is there.

One of the interesting things is that almost all of the patients with deafness whom we have seen in state hospitals throughout the State were admitted with a chief presenting complaint of impulsive and often aggressive kinds of behavior.

I think that this patient illustrates the quickness with which he can be so compliant and charming, while right underneath is this enormous tension that you can feel as he expresses himself.

The next case we want to show you is one which is even more difficult. This is a chronic paranoid girl of the schizophrenic group, who had been in and out of hospitals several times. She is a good illustration of what we were able to do here, because we were able to get her out and we were able to get her back in time to provide the intensive help required if there is to be hope of discharge again.

Dr. Abdullah:

This patient, O. I., clearly has the diagnosis of paranoid schizophrenia. In addition she is one of nonidentical twins, sisters with very different color of eyes and hair. Her twin is married and separated from her husband.

The patient is 27 years old. Her father is an alcoholic. The parents are separated, and both parents seem not to want to have anything to do with her. We have tried our best to involve them in her welfare, but all they do is get angry. They say, "It is none of our business, and why do you keep bothering us? We have our own lives to lead."

On the other hand, the parents have created a lot of confusion in her mind by writing to her and telling her, whenever they have visited her, that the moment the doctors give permission they will take her home.

When she first became delusional in 1959, she was admitted to an upstate state hospital, where she stayed for a couple of months. She was discharged, but was readmitted a few months later. When she was out again, she believed that people were talking about her and were looking and poking through the window into her bedroom. She became quite disturbed and was taken to another state hospital.

During one of her several brief trials outside of these hospitals, she was placed in a foster home with a deaf family, where she stayed until her delusions came up again. Neighbors reported that she started playing her record player very loud, and a policeman came, because the deaf couple with whom she was living didn't hear her playing the records. Next she started to become delusional with the idea that somebody was hiding in the closet, and bothering her. She was again hospitalized.

She got to us in 1964. Here she made a very good adjustment with the usual treatment. Later, we started to put her on the Fountain

House day program.[2] When an apartment was found for her she moved into it. She made a fairly good adjustment. She got a job and worked there for about 10 months.

During this period, she would sometimes get a little disturbed. When this happened, the social worker would immediately inform us, and we would go and talk to her and patch things up. Each time her disturbance was somehow related to a letter from her mother. We would talk her out of it and try to calm her down, altering or increasing the medication at times.

At the end of about 10 months, she again became very delusional. She had gone for a tooth extraction, and had perhaps received adrenalin. She got into an acute psychotic episode, we were informed, and quite late one night Mrs. Badanes and I had to go down and bring her back to the hospital. She is here now. She is again settled down, but is still delusional and suspicious. She appears to have a peculiar delusional system, in which she is afraid of certain sets of words. She believes that these words have evil power over her, and that they are responsible for her suffering.

Dr. Altshuler:

Dr. Vollenweider, do you want to comment on the psychological tests?

Dr. Vollenweider:

This patient is quite verbal. I was able to give her Rorschach, TAT, and other projective tests that I cannot give to a great many other patients because their communication ability is so poor. She achieved a performance IQ of 94, which is in the average range of intelligence. There is no indication, even though she was quite disturbed, that intellectual function was severely impaired. This, of course, is typical of paranoid schizophrenics.

There were many indications that she was psychotic, and indications of detachment. She showed occasional sharp breaks in judgment and in reality testing. There were indications that her behavior was random and disorganized. Her self-esteem was apparently very low. The projective test data suggested that she was extremely upset by both sexual and aggressive impulses, and that she tried to cope with this by denial and repression.

---

² See page 39.

There was another mechanism she appeared to use—and this has been verified by some of her relatives—that is, she tends to be very overconforming in her behavior. What is also apparent in the Rorschach and other tests is that her defenses weren't really good ones. They are rigidly maintained and could very easily fail her, and in the course of her history, this has happened quite often.

[Patient was presented.]

Question:

Has she had anything like auditory hallucinations?

Dr. Abdullah:

At present she does not have them. Her history shows that it has never been mentioned. But if your question is whether the deaf have auditory hallucinations, that is an open question.

Many of our patients say that they hear God, and that sort of thing. We have one patient who reports that he regularly talks with God. But there is a difference in what these patients mean by they hear. They perhaps lipread. Sometimes they say they lipread God. Sometimes they say they sign to God and God signs back to them. This applies to some who never had any hearing.

It may be different in people who became deaf later on in life. We had a man, deaf since the age of 10, who regularly claimed he had auditory hallucinations. Most of our patients, when they report that they hear, really mean something of quite a different quality. The connotation is slightly different. It is more like a kinesthetic or vibratory experience, I think, for example a hallucination that the people upstairs are using their vacuum cleaner machine all the time.

Another patient used to say he gets ringing in his ear whenever his wife in New York talks about him. He would suddenly say, "She is talking about me right now." We would ask, "How do you know?" He would say, "I get the ringing in my ear the moment she talks. I have the ringing now." This is the hallucination he had. It was not clear what she was saying but he knew she was talking, because of the ringing.

Question:

I am wondering, are these words which she is afraid of, or which have some magical meaning, connected with some sort of religious belief?

Dr. Abdullah:

They are, for us, very innocent words. I don't want to say them in front of the patient. [Turning to the patient.] Do you mind telling them about the words?

She is very sensitive about this. There is the word "grouch." The word "grouch" is terrifying for her. She thinks it is the cause of all her suffering, but the feeling has spread onto other words. If you open her dictionary, you will find she has pasted little pieces of paper over many words. Some of them are religious words. One was "Methodist," but there are others. There is no regular pattern, no sexual trend, no sexual symbolism. I have tried to figure it out, but it seems more or less random; and what makes her decide on the particular word, we just don't know. Even now she believes that all her troubles started with that word "grouch."

Interestingly enough, this has been consistent in her older records, also. Here it is repeated, that she is mortified by the word "grouch." She once uttered it and they put her in the State hospital. If she hears it, or if she reads it, she has to close her eyes; otherwise some calamity will fall on her. She feels she has had great trouble because of the word.

Question to Dr. Abdullah:

Does she do things occasionally for novelty in her life; you know, to break up the monotony?

Dr. Abdullah:

She doesn't like to do the same work for a long time. We have to keep changing her occupation in the hospital. She works for a short time, say, in the store, and then she wants to do homemaking. Then she wants to do cooking. She does a good job. This way she gets into new working situations. She has been in practically all of our hospital activities.

Dr. Rainer:

Has she talked about her sister lately?

Dr. Abdullah:

She talks about her. [To patient.] What about your sister? The answer is: OK, he is in the Air Force and they are separated a long time. [To patient.] Is your sister deaf? She says no. This was a great frustration.

Question to Dr. Abdullah:

Do you have data on the comparative development of the two twins? Was she the younger? What was the birth weight?

Dr. Abdullah:

She was 5 pounds when she was born, and for a long time she was in the incubator. The other one was more vigorous but this one remained sickly. Her deafness was noticed very soon, when she was about 1 year old. The other twin grew up normally. She dated; she learned; she took piano lessons. Temperamentally, they repeatedly describe her as being different. She was outgoing. This one was shut in, more introspective, partly due to her handicap. She got along very well with the sister, but as they grew up the sister had more activities, more boy friends, music and outings, and other things. The patient was left out, and so she developed a lot of hostility and feelings of inferiority; she would protest and ask why God made her deaf and not her sister, and that sort of thing.

Dr. Rainer:

She was one of a group of twins studied in our project when we were looking for twins, especially discordant twins. When she turned up with the psychosis, we looked back and found the old records, and found pictures of them taken when they were 5 or 6 years younger. On the whole, we have a fair amount of data, including psychological tests. Early data were not distinguishable as prepsychotic. About 5 years after our initial study we sent the old data back to the psychologist who had originally obtained them. He reread the tests and still felt they showed no signs of psychosis at that time. When we sent them to him, however, we knew she had had her first psychotic episode.

Question:

Was there any separation in verbal and performance functions in any of the earlier tests, or any perceptual or motor problems when she was younger?

Dr. Rainer:

I don't think there was anything in her material to show that.

Question:

Do you find anything to indicate something organic or any overcompensation? I was interested in her verbal system in relation to the problems involved in her attitude toward her verbal system, and whether or not this was a compensation for other problems in terms of special perception functions, whether these were intact.

Dr. Vollenweider:

As far as we can tell, they are pretty intact.

Dr. Altshuler:

We have tried to show you three cases with different diagnostic labels who also differ in the amount of communication skill they have. I think you can see that this girl, though she is by far the best of the three, and had many years of schooling, does not approach the facility or the ability to understand conceptual things that the people who spoke to you this morning showed. Those people are achievers. This girl represents perhaps the normal person who is diminished by the inroads of mental illness.

One thing I would like to emphasize to you, also, about the treatment we try to arrange here, is the close supervision that is given to the patients after they leave. I think it was indicated in Dr. Abdullah's report of the staff going to get this girl late at night.

We maintain a very close relationship with the Fountain House organization, or wherever we place our patients, so we can, in a sense, be aware of everything that is going on and step in when it becomes necessary.

Because of the combination of mental illness and deafness, we also keep in as close touch as possible with them when they go out in the community, and they are often taken by us to the job they are going to do. We make every effort to build up a relationship with the employer, so that the patients may be given more tolerance. Most of this contacting is done by Mrs. Badanes, who serves as vocational rehabilitation worker and general handmaiden to most of the patients.

The last patient we want to show you, J. C., is a man who was transferred here after 23 years in another hospital. I think he demonstrates more than anything else what the absence of a facility such as this can lead to—in other words, the absence of people who can evaluate the patient and communicate with him.

There is no doubt that had he not had the chance to come here, he would have stayed in a State hospital for the rest of his life. He had already been there 23 years, from about the age of 16. We were fortunate enough to be able to get him out, and working, in about three and a half months. Dr. Abdullah will tell you about him.

Dr. Abdullah:

In the summer of 1965, Dr. Vollenweider and I went upstate, visiting many of the State hospitals there, and we landed at this particular hospital. We were tired after a long journey. After lunch, we started seeing the deaf patients. After talking to one young fellow, we saw another one, a backward patient, who had been 23 years in that hospital. He was dressed in baggy hospital garb, and was sitting alone in the corner.

We just talked with him. Perhaps because we were at that time quite selective, picking out those with rehabilitation potential whom we thought we could rehabilitate, we thought, "Well, this a patient, to be sure, and there isn't much we can do about him. He's just a chronic hospitalized, institutionalized patient."

But then we added, "Let's consider him." He talked nicely; he was quite friendly; something moved us. We finally decided to include him in the list of those we want in the hospital.

When he came here we had the same reaction. We felt that here's a patient of about 40 who got to the State hospital at the age of 16. We felt he wouldn't be much of a candidate, but at least we would give him a try.

What we got was a miracle! In 2 months' time he was transformed from a chronic institutionalized patient; he just blossomed into a full person. And this was so from almost the very first day.

What happened was that he suddenly had an audience. In the group, he took over the group. On the ward, he took over the ward. He was everybody's older brother. He was so witty, so communicative, so full of stories and anecdotes, that patients were always gathered around him. He blossomed, veritably. It seemed he had not talked for many years, and yet he became a prime candidate for rehabilitation.

On closer study we found that he was remarkably well preserved in his personality. He had very good manners. He knew how to talk with people.

The family history is that everybody drinks. There is a borderline alcoholic mother and a father beyond that border. The rest of his history can be summed up in the two words "running away."

He always ran away. He ran away from school, he ran away from home, he ran away from one school to another. He ran away from the job in which he was placed. He ran away to a relative. That was his sole form of protest. Whenever he had a difficulty, whenever he felt unhappy, he ran away. He ran away from one State hospital to go south, and then got himself admitted to a State hospital there. His record is thick with accounts of his escapades and the details about them; the hospital in Texas contacted New York, and he was brought back by limousine.

This was the only way he could get any attention; he had found by running out that people fussed about him. Once he was back on the ward, there was nothing for him to do and he just drifted. Then something would pep him up and he would run away and people would fuss.

His diagnosis at the hospital where we found him was psychosis due to organic causes, yet we found him remarkably free of any psychotic tendencies, and there were no delusions or illusions. He generally had good judgment and a very good sense of humor.

Mrs. Badanes will tell us the rest of the story.

Mrs. Badanes:

Actually, this patient's job placement is the most classic example of selective placement. This man had been hospitalized for 23 years; he was accustomed to living in an institution. So he needed something special. And this something special came up one day. Previously, Reverend Jasper had helped us place one of our outpatients at a college near New York City. This girl had worked out so well that when a job became available in the kitchen, we were asked if we had anybody who could fill this job. It was a job where there was also a place to live in.

Of course, I immediately thought of this man. He had worked in a hospital kitchen for many years, and here was an outside job doing similar work. It was in an institution; as such, it was not going to be so different for him. He would have some kind of supervision and living, and it was a job he had had experience in doing and could do.

We took the patient over right away. He met the person who was in charge of the kitchen. He explained what he could do. The pay was great; he had never made this kind of money. It was living and board, and something like $250 a month, and he was just thrilled at the idea. After the first interview, we brought him over to stay, and from that day on, he has been simply marvelous.

At the present time, this running away of his has become more acceptably channeled. When he has any vacation time, no matter how brief, he will take ridiculously long trips. Last week, when we went to see him, to tell him we would bring him here today, he explained he had just returned from Iowa where he had gone to see his sister, only she wasn't there.

He had known that she had lived there years before, and he hadn't seen her in years. He wrote her a letter, had it mailed, and immediately upon having written, he simply went. He didn't bother to wait for an answer.

When he got there, of course, she wasn't there. He had spent 46 hours on a bus, but he adored the trip. He wasn't the least bit upset at having made the long trip and not finding her. And now he can return on his own. Later, he found his sister living in Rochester, and he did get to visit her. We are frequently surprised to learn that he took a trip for a day to go see somebody 150 miles away. The point worth emphasizing though, is that he comes back of his own accord.

The other fascinating thing is, that if he gets the least bit upset or depressed on the job, he turns up here. He tells them where he is going, and he doesn't run off when he is supposed to be working. He is very diligent about the work he does. But when he is upset, he simply comes here, tells us what is on his mind, and gets reassured. We go and visit him again soon after, to be sure that everything is all right.

[Patient was presented.]

Dr. Abdullah:

Since he has taken this job, this patient has run away twice, and both times he came here. Once he came because he had a cold and was not feeling well. We gave him a couple of aspirins, and he went back.

Today he told me that 2 weeks ago he came here because he had gone for a tooth extraction and it was so painful that he wanted to tell me about it. He just stopped me in the hall now and told me.

Question:

How did things go in the hospital?

Dr. Abdullah:

Unfortunately, as things are, in the other State hospital he could not be included in psychotherapy. He just drifted into the back ward. Nobody had any plans for him. On his records, the first few sheets were filled with escapes.

He always got into the limelight whenever he did that sort of thing. That he was, otherwise, an ideal patient, has been mentioned a good many times. He was no problem in the State hospital. He did a good job in the kitchen, he bothered nobody, and nobody bothered him.

Question:

Do you have any idea of what happened in the prior 23 years in the hospital that enabled him to remain intact?

Dr. Altshuler:

We just don't know the answer to that question.

I think I should emphasize that this is the patient who had been hospitalized the longest. We have seen several patients, however, who, at the very least, were misdiagnosed and, at the very most, have remained up to 6 or 8 years in a hospital without the necessity for continuous hospitalization. Anyone who is interested enough to make a survey of the patients in their State hospitals could perform an important service, namely, to correct the misdiagnoses and to make some arrangements for those people who could be treated.

Dr. Abdullah:

Recently, in the group meeting, this patient threw in advice about what is the best way of leaving the hospital. He still thinks himself as a model; having lived over 20 years in hospitals, he knows all about the mechanics and the culture of the State hospital.

Question to Patient:

What was the final straw that made you run away from the other hospital?

Patient:

I wanted a job.

Dr. Abdullah:

He wanted some change. [To patient.] But you ran away to another State hospital in Texas. Why? You can't get a job there.

Patient:

I didn't want to run away from the Texas hospital. They put me back in the hospital in New York State.

Dr. Abdullah to Patient:

Why did you run away to Texas to the State Hospital? Why?

Patient:

I didn't go there. I was going to Williamsburg, Va., to visit my friend's father and mother, but I gave up. The police put me to Texas State Hospital, for waiting to go back.

Dr. Abdullah:

He says that he didn't go to the other State hospital. He went to meet the parents of his friends some place, but then he gave up. He gave up because he ran short of money and he went to the police and said, "I am from a State hospital." They put him into the nearest State hospital. That is what he explains. Then they sent him back.

Question to Dr. Abdullah:

How does he feel being in front of the group here this afternoon?

Patient:

Fine.

Dr. Abdullah:

The interesting thing is when he was leaving the ward, we had a party, a farewell party, and we asked him to give a little talk. The poise and the manner in which he spoke, was one of the best speeches we had ever heard from one of our patients. He spoke very nicely, and was quite moving in his speech, I thought.

Dr. Vollenweider:

I want to add that, in this job David has, he is very good about saving money and putting it in the bank. He gets $250 a month and saves about $248. He has almost $900 saved.

Dr. Abdullah:

He gets board and lodging. He sometimes gives presents. What are you saving for?

Patient:

To give away.

Dr. Abdullah:

He does give presents to patients when he comes here.

Question to Dr. Abdullah:

Is he planning to run away again?

Dr. Abdullah:

Are you planning to run away from work?

Patient:

No.

Dr. Abdullah:

Why not? He is still visiting the State hospital where he used to be. He goes to visit his friends there, other patients. He is very friendly and affectionate and a warm person. He enjoys traveling. Do you still go to visit the hospital upstate?

Patient:

Yes, sometimes.

Question:

How do you get along with the students at the college?

Patient:

Fine.

Question:

Do you tease the students sometimes?

Patient:

Yes, and they tease me, too.

Dr. Abdullah:

He was complaining about the salt shaker here and there—very messy, and all that. Aside from that running away business, he once in a while visits and talks to people on Sundays. He comes here and sometimes gives a dollar to someone.

Question to Patient:

Do you want to say something?

Patient:

At college, sometimes, they put sugar upside down. I can't pick it up. I work to clean the tables and the sugar falls on the floor.

Dr. Altshuler:

Thank you very much.

Discussion

Dr. Altshuler:

Our policy has been that we make at least a yearly trip to each of the 21 State hospitals in the State of New York to renew our acquaintanceship with deaf patients who are there; we try to review the case with the staff of the hospital, and pick up any new cases that have been admitted since our previous visit.

Just recently we have been able to obtain an official ruling permitting us to transfer here, temporarily, patients from one of the other hospitals when we have an empty bed on the ward. The length of time is decided by how long we think it will take to do whatever we can for them. If we cannot help them, then we are able to return them to the hospital from which they originated. That will give us, in the next 2 years, a chance to rotate many of the 300 cases in the State through the unit.

Question to Dr. Abdullah:

Do you find that your deaf patients respond to psychotropic medication any differently from hearing patients?

Dr. Abdullah:

I don't think so; not the psychotics. But we have been able to take many of the patients off of psychotropic medication. With the last patient you saw, we put him on a small amount of tranquilizer before he left because we were afraid of how he would react. We were more afraid than he was, because we felt it would be a new experience for him. We put him on a very small dose.

We have found that some of the brain damaged cases are supersensitive to phenothiazines, and some—in whom we had been certain of brain damage—had oculogyric crises. In such cases phenothiazines can almost be used for diagnosis.

Question:

In your group of 300 patients, do you find a variety of disturbances that differ from the normal or hearing patient population?

Dr. Altshuler:

Yes, we do. We will be talking about that tomorrow. The preponderance of them are schizophrenic, with the same proportion that you would find in the hearing population. There are some from the manic depressive and cycloid groups, but we very seldom see a retarded depression. Cases in the manic depressive and involutional groups usually show the more agitated forms of depression, or are paranoid in their presentations.

There seem to be, on the basis of the State hospital files, fewer alcoholics. We also haven't seen many alcoholics in the outpatient clinic.

There is an increase of certain organic illnesses, like retinitis pigmentosa, which causes mental deficiency, as well as deafness and blindness. At times the triad goes together with psychosis.

There is also an increase in the category, psychosis with mental deficiency, even after we changed the diagnosis in misdiagnosed cases. I think that is because there are a number of cases that became deaf through illness that leave brain damage as well as deafness, thus leading to mental deficiency. If such persons should later become psychotic, you have a psychosis with mental deficiency. Otherwise the diagnostic distributions are quite similar for deaf and hearing.

Question:

The young man who was sitting at the corner, who had had 1 year of college, has he been catatonic?

Dr. Abdullah:

Yes. He is slightly better.

Dr. Rainer:

When he first came to this ward, transferred from another ward, we thought we had another one of the miraculous improvements. He came in catatonic, and within a week or 2 weeks he was playing ping-pong with other patients and was the champion of the ward. But he slipped down again; he has had a few little rises since then. He is now in a little better rise.

Question:

During group therapy session I noticed the patient we last saw saying that he behaved, that he listened to the nurses. In what context was he saying that?

Dr. Abdullah:

It was in a discussion of a patient for whom discharge was not in sight. From his long experience in State hospitals he learned the rules for getting along with the staff—obey the nurses and go to the occupational therapy regularly, and work. He is an expert on how to make out in an institution.

Question:

Was he recommending this advice to her?

Dr. Abdullah:

Yes. These are the common rules to follow to get out of the hospital.

Theoretical Considerations in Development and Psychopathology of the Deaf

Dr. Kenneth Z. Altshuler

Dr. Rainer:

The New York Psychiatric Institute, where we are meeting today, is the key research and teaching institution for the New York State Department of Mental Hygiene. It is operated by the State of New York, as are Rockland State Hospital, where you were yesterday, and the other 20 or so State hospitals throughout the State.

This Institute is primarily a research and teaching institution. It also has a small clinical service, and a community mental health program and serves as the center of psychiatric teaching for the College of Physicians and Surgeons of Columbia Medical School, across the street, which is part of the Columbia-Presbyterian Medical Center. The staff of the institute hold dual appointments with New York State and with Columbia University. There are a half-dozen or so research departments—such as biochemistry, experimental psychology, as well as the Department of Medical Genetics which is our department, and the one under whose aegis this entire deafness work has been going on since 1955.

Dr. Lawrence C. Kolb, professor of Psychiatry at Columbia, and director of the Psychiatric Institute, wished me to express his regrets that he couldn't be here to welcome you in person this morning. Prior important engagements unfortunately made it impossible for him, but he wants you to know of his interest in this work and his appreciation that you have come here. To begin our program, Dr. Altshuler will talk about theoretical considerations in the psychopathology of the deaf. This afternoon we will allow time for any discussion which you may wish to contribute.

Dr. Altshuler:

We can approach the theoretical considerations in the area of deafness from two viewpoints: One would have to do with the effects, if

65

any, of deafness on personality structure and how these effects might be mediated. Secondly, we can consider the implications of studies of the deaf for psychiatric or psychoanalytic theory.

The work of our projects in New York has been concerned with the effects of the handicap on the deaf, and also with what we as psychiatrists or theoreticians can extract from this population that would be of interest and value in the field. So I will begin by telling you something of what we have done, and also what remains to be done— which is much greater, and of which I hope you will become a part.

It is obvious that the primary limitation of deafness is the auditory input, and that whatever the other consequences are, they derive in some way from this initial limitation.

Deafness interferes directly with the mother-child relationship, for if either the parent or child is deaf, communication with each other is limited. Indirectly deafness interferes by way of the feelings that are evoked in the mother who has an affected child. Bowlby,[1] for example, has told us that auditory contact forms a very intimate part of the child's bond to his mother, and that a baby can be quieted when he is only a few weeks old if he can hear mother's voice, even from the next room. This auditory contact is lost to the deaf child.

Another thing which I think is important in the relationship of parent to child in the presence of deafness, is the misguided advice that parents often get, to the effect that they should not use any type of language with the children except speech. In the end this amounts to what you might call a sort of double bind, where the message is "I won't communicate with you (the child) because I love you and ultimately want you to be able to learn to speak." Actually, however, this attitude can make for separation between parent and child if carried to an extreme.

Obviously, the absence of audition also interferes with the development of speech and language. This means that these functions don't come into play in personality development at the time in which they normally would be expected to. While deafness, of course, doesn't make anyone stupid, the retarded language development leads to a functional retardation in many deaf persons. For example, the students who graduate from a school for the deaf at the age of 17 or 18 function, on the average, at a fourth-grade level of reading, or maybe on a fifth-grade level in arithmetic.

The important consequences of this absence of audition and language are that there is a lack of conceptual tools for the child to use to codify

---

[1] Bowlby, J. The nature of the child's tie to his mother. *Int. J. Psychoanalysis, 39:* 350, 1958.

and synthesize his experiences, and he does not have the conceptual or symbolic hooks on which to hang his experiences.[2] A number of studies have indicated that as a result there are some kinds of defects in abstraction. This has been the broadest finding, although the absolute definition of what these defects are is still a matter of speculation. They have been listed variously as defects in evolving symbolic relations, in recollection of similarities, and in deduction of consequences.

What is of interest to us is that a number of these abilities to manipulate symbols may be important for evolving a sense of feeling for other people, and perhaps even for exercising self control.

Traditionally, and I believe quite correctly, all these problems have been attacked by an emphasis on early education. With the communication barrier present, educators are faced with a vast and demanding task, to get the information into the children. As a result, a sort of dependency is fostered in the children who become used to being spoon fed. Unfortunately, there is not enough time remaining to encourage their own free-wheeling development or independent creative thinking.

Frank Withrow, whom I mentioned yesterday as starting a curriculum of social hygiene, has been trying to get across some information on sex and genetics. He noted that in the beginning the students almost refused to participate, because they wanted and expected the teacher just to tell them. The teacher would ask them questions and demand that they put out some kind of independent thought. This they were reluctant to do.[3]

In addition, there are the usual effects of residential schooling. Long separations from home are involved and the children are segregated by sex; whatever the effects of these aspects of residential education may be, most of our deaf children have been exposed to them. As far as I know, there is no way to tease apart and clearly allocate a particular effect to any of these factors individually. This remains a persistent and important challenge.

There can be no doubt, however, that the overall effect of deafness is a stressful one. Because of its wide and durable impact on personality development, it could perhaps be expected to wipe out some individual differences. That is, the very universality of this stress on all sectors of development would lead, I think, to some similarity in people affected.

Within the limits to which any generalization is true, we had noted certain definite aspects of character in the deaf adult population with

---

[2] For a full treatment of these aspects see Altshuler, K. Z. Personality traits and depressive symptoms in the deaf, in *Recent Advances in Biological Psychiatry*, Vol. 6 (J. Wortis, ed.). New York, Plenum Press, 1964.

[3] Withrow, F. Illinois School for the Deaf, Jacksonville, Ill. Personal communication.

whom we come in contact. These were particularly clear in the neurotic patients in our outpatient clinic, and of course, even more emphasized in psychotic groups.

But we concluded that even in our interviews with normal patients and normal subjects, we could detect certain similarities. These included what we might call a lack of understanding and regard for the feelings of other people; I suppose it is summarized in the term "lack of empathy." It is a lessened awareness of the impact of their own behavior on other people and its consequences, and the tendency to impulsive behavior with a kind of limited control.

I do not mean to say that conscience is necessarily impaired. I think these people have excellent consciences, but there is, in many of our people, something about the control of impulse which, even without brain damage, seems to be limited. As the pressure for impulse builds up, the controls and constraints that are available somehow are not up to the task.

One thought we came upon when we were reviewing what the stresses of deafness were, was that in many ways it seemed to resemble some of of the theories that were advanced about the genesis of schizophrenia. For example, this idea I referred to, that "I won't talk to you because I care for you," smacked to us of the double bind.[4] The whole disturbance in the parent-child relationship, with the increase in the maternal guilt feelings, or wishes for rejection, or denial of the real needs and limitations of the children—all this sounded to us like the sort of thing that had been described in schizophrenogenic mothers.

The fact that, where conceptual growth was involved, physical development went on quite normally while psychological development was necessarily slowed down, sounded, we thought like Bender's [5] idea of uneven development in sectors of personality or an imbalance between development and maturation.

We thought that this would be a good group in which to see whether or not schizophrenia is found with an increased frequency. We thought that this group could be used in that way to test the old genetic-environmental question in schizophrenia.

What we did was to study all the siblings of the schizophrenic deaf subjects that we found in our State hospitals. There were some 331 individual siblings, of, I believe, 138 cases.

The idea, here, was that if the deafness had indirectly contributed to the development of schizophrenia in the children, then the siblings

---

[4] Bateson, G. et al. Toward a theory of schizophrenia. *Behav. Sci., 1:* 251, 1956.
[5] Bender, L. The concept of plasticity in childhood schizophrenia. In *Psychopathology of Schizophrenia* (P. Hoch & J. Zubin, Eds.). New York, Grune & Stratton, 1960.

would be just like the siblings of any other normal group of people, and they should have a schizophrenia rate which would come very close to that for the general population.

On the other hand, if the gene structure had somehow been the necessary agent for the development of the schizophrenic process, then the siblings of the index cases would have the same likelihood of developing the disease as the siblings of any other group of schizophrenics.

The results of the study and some of the problems along the way can best be reported with the aid of a few tables. The first (table 1)

TABLE 1

DISTRIBUTION OF SCHIZOPHRENIC HOSPITAL PATIENTS IN NEW YORK STATE ACCORDING TO LENGTH OF HOSPITALIZATION

Hospitalized Schizophrenics In New York State		Percentage Of Schizophrenics Hospitalized:		
Hearing Status	Total	Less Than 5 Years	5 Years And Over	20 Years And Over
Hearing*	52,225	24.2	75.8	35.4
Deaf	120	10.8	89.2	47.5

*State Of New York, Department Of Mental Hygiene, Annual Report, 1957

shows one of the difficulties we ran into. In the beginning, we thought we would take a count of schizophrenics in the hospitals, compare the number of deaf among them with the number of hearing, put both of these over the denominators of the total populations in the State (deaf and hearing), and then we would come up with a schizophrenia rate for the deaf, and one for the hearing.[6]

It turned out that, calculated this way, the deaf had about 2½ times the percent frequency of schizophrenia as the hearing. When we

---

[6] Actually even this method, the abridged Weinberg method, involved certain assumptions about age of risk and the ratio of hospitalized to nonhospitalized patients. These are omitted for the sake of brevity in this presentation. For a fuller treatment see Rainer, J. D. and Kallmann, F. J. Genetic and demographic aspects of disordered behavior patterns in a deaf population. In *Epidemiology of Mental Disorder* (B. Pasamanick, ed.). Washington, AAAS, 1959, and Altshuler, K. Z. and Sarlin, M. B. Deafness and schizophrenia: Interrelation of communication stress, maturation lag and schizophrenic risk. In *Expanding Goals of Genetics in Psychiatry* (F. J. Kallmann, ed.). New York, Grune & Stratton, 1962.

looked at it more closely, the problem was that deaf patients tended to stay in the hospital longer; for example, if you had 10 people in the hospital, and instead of two of them getting discharged this year and two new ones coming in, the first two stayed on, and then two new ones came in and the same thing happened the following year, you would soon end up with 14 or 16 deaf schizophrenic patients in the hospital, yielding an unrealistically high numerator, and therefore an overstated frequency rate. This kind of a comparison, then, would not be valid.

The table demonstrates that the percentage of deaf schizophrenics who are hospitalized 20 years and over is greater than the percentage for the hearing, namely, 47 percent to 35 percent, and the same holds true for 5 years and over—89 percent to 75 percent; whereas most of the hearing schizophrenics were hospitalized for less than 5 years.

Table 2 represents a general review of the various genetic studies of schizophrenia that have been done. The first column is frequency in the general population. We use as our comparison the Kallmann, 1946 study since he used a New York State population, just as we did, and the diagnostic criteria he employed were conservative and comparable to our own.

TABLE 2

FREQUENCY OF SCHIZOPHRENIA
IN THE GENERAL POPULATION AND IN RELATIVES OF SCHIZOPHRENICS

SOURCE	Frequency Of Schizophrenia In General Population	Frequency Of Schizophrenia In The Relatives Of One Schizophrenic					
		Stepsibs	Half Sibs	Full Sibs	Dizygotic Cotwins	Monozygotic Cotwins	Parents
Various Investigations (1916 to 1953)	0.3–2.4	—	7.6	4.5–12.0	12.5–14.9	68.3–81.7	7.1–12.0
Kallmann 1946 (twin index cases)	0.85	1.8	7.0	14.3	14.7	85.8	9.2

Let us look at the findings. Frequency in the general population is a little less than 1 percent. Note that as a person becomes more genetically like an index case who has schizophrenia, the likelihood of his incurring the disease increases stepwise. With monozygotic twins, one of whom is schizophrenic, the likelihood of schizophrenia in the cotwin is 86 percent. With full siblings, it is about 14 percent. In other words, if a person is schizophrenic, of his siblings—if he had 100 of them—about 14 are likely to develop the disease.

Table 3 is a summary of the study that we did, and the last column mostly tells the story. The siblings of deaf schizophrenics throughout the state had a schizophrenia expectancy rate of about 11 percent.

TABLE 3

SCHIZOPHRENIC RISK DATA
IN THE SIBLINGS OF DEAF AND HEARING SCHIZOPHRENICS

	Number Of Siblings		Corrected Frame Of Reference	Crude Risk (%)	Corrected Risk (%)
	Surviving Age 15	Definitely Schizophrenic			
Of Deaf Index Cases:					
Hearing Sibs	303	25	223	8.3	11.2
Deaf Sibs*	28	3	19	10.7	15.8
Total	331	28	242	8.5	11.6**
Of Hearing Index Cases (Kallman 1946):	2014	184	1288	9.14	14.3

* Includes Seven Cases With Marked Hearing Loss
** 14.1% If Probable Cases Are Included

There is no significant difference between the rate for hearing siblings, 11 percent, and that for the deaf siblings of the index cases, 15.8 percent. None of these risk figures differed significantly from the 14 percent rate for sibs of hearing schizophrenics (Kallmann's 1946 study).

We had hoped in the beginning that by the comparison of hearing and deaf siblings (of the deaf schizophrenics) we would be able to define what really was a quantified rate of the impact of deafness. The impact apparently was not very much, although there is an indication that deafness is somewhat more of a stress. In other words, this study indicates that whatever other impact deafness may have on personality development, at least it does not seem to have an appreciable influence on the likelihood of one's developing schizophrenia.

Another finding with several theoretical implications was suggested almost accidentally. We were reviewing the cases both in our outpatient clinic and among the inpatients, for the frequency of various symptomatology. What emerged was a singular absence of retarded depression in either group.

When we look over our case material, we found we had at that time some 300 patients in the outpatient department. And we had roughly between 250 and 300 people that we had seen as inpatients. There were no more than two cases of what you might call a true, retarded depression; in other words, where the person looks down, shows psychomotor retardation, does not respond when you question him—things of that sort, which we associate with the psychotic depression.

Instead, these cases showed a paranoid form of depression, or a very anxious, agitated presentation, but without the mea culpa content seem among the hearing, the self recriminations and excessive sense of guilt.

We wondered why this should be, and I think we could be reasonably sure that we were not missing cases. They weren't disappearing into the hands of the private practitioner and not coming to us, for we had very good contact with most of the deaf population. If these cases did exist, they should have shown up, one way or another, either as inpatients or on our clinic rolls.

You will recall that Freud said that depressions are a splitting of the superego in which one part proceeds to berate the other.[7] This was clarified by the work of Abraham [8] and Rado [9] who recast what happens in depression in terms of psychodynamics. These authors called attention to a premelancholic phase of coercive resentment towards a love object.

According to Rado, the course of this melancholic resentment determines the quality of the subsequent depression. When the rage fails to regain the magical services of the object, the adaptive method of repentance may be invoked. This involves a great deal of chest beating, sense of guilt, and so forth.

The idea here is that self punishment will bring forgiveness and love, and therefore re-evoke the assistance of the love object, and so the rage is impounded and internalized, and turns against oneself. The whole process of guilty expiation, ironically, still continues to serve the primary goal of coercing the love object. The clinical picture then depends on the balance that is established between guilt, rage and fear. If guilt predominates, you get the guilty berating of oneself. If the rage is so frightening to the individual that it must be totally repressed, then you get the retarded depression with its constricted general function; whereas if just fear of direct expression of this coercive rage is present, you get the more agitated depression, as the rage bubbles to the surface, is barely held in check, and evokes anxiety.

[7] Freud, S. Mourning and melancholia. In *Collected Papers,* Vol. 4. London, Hogarth Press, 1925.

[8] Abraham, K. Manic-depressive states and the pregenital levels of the libido. In *Collected Papers on Psychoanalysis.* London, Hogarth Press, 1927.

[9] Rado, S. Psychodynamics of depression from the etiologic point of view. *Psychosom. Med., 13:* 51, 1951.

Under certain conditions you would not expect to see a retarded guilt in depression. For example, it should not occur when the control machinery of the individual is limited and when impulsivity predominates; so that tensions are discharged in action, rather than contained through intrapsychic maneuvers. This is what is seen in the deaf, for the most part. Thus, the absence of this type of depression in our deaf population seems to us to be a kind of indirect confirmation of some of the psychoanalytic descriptions in the theory of depression.

The underlying idea would be that language, or the closeness of contact which it brings, plays some role in the internalization of rage and the ability to impose constraints upon oneself, and that this process may be limited in deaf subjects; therefore, instead of a retarded depression developing, we get either a paranoid form or the more agitated one, in which the rage is very close to being acted out. In talking to some of these subjects, we find that the rage is very close to the surface, and the main feeling you derive is that they are angry and afraid of their anger, rather than that they are depressed.

While the method of arriving at this confirmation of analytic theory was somewhat devious, we felt that the questions were important enough to study as best we could. All of us who are in practice work in some way, directly or indirectly, with psychoanalytic propositions, but it is a theory that has so far defied scientific confirmation of most of its tenets.

There are a number of other questions of theoretical interest in working with the deaf. One is the question about auditory hallucinations. Dr. Abdullah, I think, at an earlier session, gave you the answer insofar as we have it.[10] There is, to begin with, the question of what an hallucination is, anyhow. Certain visual hallucinations can be induced with drugs, where you get, for example, measurable EEG changes. We have not seen reports of auditory hallucinations in the literature which show anything measurable.

As Dr. Adbullah said, if the subject has had hearing, we would guess that he might have something which would resemble an auditory hallucination. If he has not, one might assume that all he can have is an hallucination of what he conceives of as audition, since he never experienced it.

Figure 1 is a picture drawn by a man who had become deaf at the age of 13 months; the picture represents his conception, during a psychotic episode, of how he heard the voice of God. You can see that some voice comes in through the ears and some of it comes through wires

---

[10] See page 51.

FIGURE 1

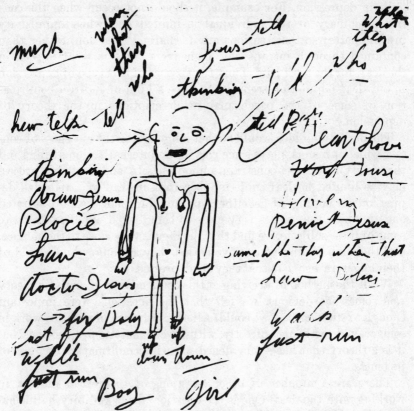

up from the heart and down to the wrists and ankles. The figure also shows the words that God is saying to him. From this picture, we would judge that the hallucination is primarily a vibratory one. This is what most of our patients who claim to have auditory hallucinations, really show us.

Also of some interest is the question of paranoia, one we are almost always asked about when discussing our deaf patients. We do not find that there is increased frequency of paranoia among those with early deafness. The paranoid stereotype is a person who loses his hearing in adulthood, and who therefore begins to think he is missing things and becomes suspicious and embarrassed. Those we see with early total deafness tend, as a group, to be much more trusting, and I don't think that as a group they could be classified as paranoids.

A question of greater interest—and here is something that we haven't begun to touch on, and certainly ideas on this would be very important—is the quality of the paranoid delusions that may develop in any paranoid case. For example, do complex systematized delusions

require the presence of language for their evolution? I have a hunch—
but only a hunch—that they may.

Even more important might be the question of the dynamic bases
or the quality of paranoid delusions. You are undoubtedly familiar
with Freud's famous characterization of paranoid delusion as developing in terms of "I, a man love him, a man," and the various transforma-
tions of the subject, verb, and/or object. It is no longer accepted that
homosexuality is the sole and sufficient basis of all paranoia. But the
basic statement might be changed so that instead of "I love a man," it
could be that I want to depend on, or I want to dominate or control
the power of either a man or a woman, with various manipulations of
the subject, verb, and/or object.[11] From this there are complex or
simple ways in which one can develop paranoid difficulty.

For example, a complicated and yet not uncommon way would be
that someone has an aggressive motivation to dominate someone else;
he fears that because of his own aggression he will be retaliated against,
and so he represses his aggression and projects it onto the other man,
who he then feels is after him, or whom he wants to force into homosexual submission. This is typical of a complicated way for paranoid
delusions to evolve.

An example of a more simply rooted paranoid development, say,
on the basis of dependency and its frustration, would be that, if I want
something from you and you don't give it to me, you don't like me.
Therefore, you hate me. This, it seems to me, is more often the kind
of thing that is involved in our deaf patients. We do not, however, have
either a nose count or any way to really establish with certainty precisely what is involved, because of the language problems. We are able
to get an idea or a feeling of whether the patient is paranoid, but often
you cannot get a clear statement of what the delusion or its bases are.
If we could have a methodology to attack this area, it would undoubtedly yield a valuable harvest for us as psychiatric theoreticians.

Several other areas of theoretical interest can be approached in
working with the deaf. One is the fact that the altered language development and the manual language itself may result in symbolic associative paths that are different for the deaf than for the hearing.
These altered associative paths could mean that events may be experienced differently by certain deaf persons, or that an emotional frame
of reference developed on these pathways may differ from the frame
of reference of the hearing.

---

[11] For the theoretical derivation of these changes see Ovesey, L. Pseudohomosexuality, the
paranoid mechanism and paranoia : An adaptational revision of a classical Freudian theory,
Psychiatry, 18 : 163, 1955.

For example, Schein [12] did a word association study with educated deaf youngsters, and he found that the deaf gave similar responses to those of the hearing, as primary associations, for only about 40 percent of the words of the Rosanoff list. This is only a beginning study, but it indicates that for the deaf the word, at least, leads to a different pathway, that it takes one off in a different direction, and so the whole thread of associations to any stimulation may be different.

I fully realize the limitation of that statement. At this point I am talking about words, but perhaps other experiences which are organized around words will also lead to different associations in the deaf and in the hearing, and therefore will have a different cognitive-emotional meaning. This, too, I think, has practically unlimited importance for use as theoreticians in the field of normal development.

In our own work, in the course of therapy, we have had to be alert for some of the differing associative threads. One woman, for example, who came into therapy for a marital problem, caused in part by her sexual frigidity, told of having a dream that a group of birds were invading her household; in the dream, she stamped out these birds very vigorously, and they were frightening to her. After this, she found that she was able to have sex with her husband, but she was no longer able to kiss him.

Figure 2 is a drawing by the patient of one of the birds. It is clearly a phallic drawing, and it is obvious why this was the bird she was stamping out and getting rid of in her house. But the question is, why

FIGURE 2

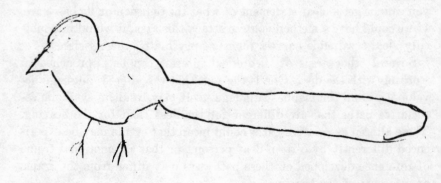

---

[12] Schein, J. Word association conformity in deaf and hearing college students. Presented at American Psychological Association meeting, New York City, 1961.

was it that after having this dream she could have sex with her husband but couldn't kiss him?

We puzzled about that for quite a while. Then it came to us—and I think this is the correct interpretation for she seemed to accept it, and it led to an alteration in the intensity of the symptoms. In sign language the sign for *kiss* and *bird* are very similar.

At all events, this was a sort of symbolic demonstration of how the associative pathways might be different. This similarity in signs was the vehicle for this patient's displacement upwards of the phobic avoidance. But the extent to which such different pathways may influence cognitive experiences and the integration of experience, have not been touched upon at all.

A final area of interest, already noted to you during these 2 days, is that the traumatic effects of early deafness are sufficiently severe as a problem to cut across individual differences and to result in certain common shared traits. This is, I believe, one of the most fascinating areas of our subject. As an extension of this finding, we hope also to get into the study of whether or not parents who are deaf, who have congenital or early acquired deafness will therefore have certain qualities in common, will then influence their hearing offspring in any way that would make them (the children) consistently different from, say, a random cross section of the hearing population.

We rather expect we may get into such a study in the next 4 or 5 years. It was really brought to my attention by the fact that I met some of the children of deaf parents and had also had two of them in treatment as private patients. They were probably the nicest people I have ever met. There was in them a kind of unusual willingness to be helpful, and an interest in other people—along with certain problems, to be sure. It would be interesting to see whether this hunch is generalizable, and whether being brought under the aegis of two parents who have both deafness and the specific qualities of character that go with it, can result in different personality structures in the offspring.

To sum up, I have tried to touch on a few aspects of psychiatric theory which may help in an understanding of the deaf, and on areas where knowledge of deafness may amplify or enhance our own theoretical certainty as psychiatrists. From even this cursory treatment it should be clear that, just as psychiatry has much to offer the deaf, so too, the deaf have very, very much to offer us as psychiatrists.

Dr. Rainer:

The conference is now open for discussion of any of these points.

Dr. Paltrow:

Have you heard of people who are partially deaf having auditory delusions?

Dr. Altshuler:

I don't see any reason why it should not occur, though I myself have not seen such patients.

Dr. Schlesinger:

There are informal reports about some of the adult deaf taking LSD in California and developing auditory delusions or hallucinations, but they are purely anecdotal.

Participant

You mentioned that the deaf lose the input of the emotional cues, the lullabies, and the other vocal phenomena associated with the emotional expression between mother and child, and they lose language. In addition, they also lose the distance cues and the spatial cues that are mediated by sound. Today, with the interesting work that is being done in echo location, it is becoming much clearer that these are essential cues for certain aspects of early ego formation.

I am wondering whether perhaps some of the loss of input, very early in life, might not also result in some perceptual ego distortions in this area. The whole attitude toward danger, toward interpersonal distance and territoriality, in a person who is unable to perceive auditory danger signals, would seem to be a very basic thing.

The totally deaf mother also appears to be less responsive to the infant, even though she may be seeing the crying behavior of the infant. There is something uniquely imprinting, as far as the maternal response is concerned, which has to do with the auditory signal.

Dr. Boston:

Was there any difference in the psychopathology of people with middle ear deafness, compared with cochlear or nerve disease?

Dr. Altshuler:

To date we have not studied our group from that viewpoint.

Dr. Brummit:

Hearing teenagers frequently think that someone is calling them, and they investigate. Do you have the same thing in deaf children, and if so, does it occur more frequently or less frequently? In the hearing, it is a very common teenage phenomenon.

Dr. Altshuler:

I have never asked our teenagers directly about that but I have not been impressed with any increase in frequency.

Dr. Brummit:

It is usually the thought that a parent is calling them.

Participant:

I was going to say it is my impression that teenagers more often have the impression that someone is *not* calling them!

Question:

I would like to return to the question raised about character structure; I think there is a correlation between yesterday's presentation of the group therapy, and some of Dr. Robinson's work, which I hope he will get a chance to tell us about. The statement has been made that deaf people can be insensitive to the feelings of others. Perhaps what we are talking about is our insensitivity about their sensitivity. I think hearing people may be the ones who don't know. When you see deaf people in groups and hear about their experiences in groups, I think what one is impressed with is that one deaf person picks up the feelings of the other deaf person. I think it may be a barrier between the hearing and the deaf, rather than, necessarily, a character structure defect in the deaf. That is the impression I get from listening to them.

Dr. Altshuler:

That strikes me as a very good point. Of course, before we accuse someone of not understanding, we must be clear that they have had the opportunity to understand. If we say they are not attentive to the feelings of other people, we must be certain that we have at least given them the chance to have the picture flashed to them—whether they pick it up or not. Then and then only can we decide what to say about it.

I didn't have the time to go into a number of case histories. I think, however, that we have seen it often enough where the context is clear, where one would expect that there would be an awareness, a greater awareness, of the other person's feelings than we have actually seen in a number of particular instances.

Dr. Rainer:

This comes out specifically in marital counseling of deaf couples, where I think we have a fairly good sense of what the degree of understanding between husband and wife should be. In our deaf couples, I have seen some big gaps in one spouse's understanding of the problems and the difficulties of the other.

Dr. Boston:

You mentioned the need for physical contact between people in one of the cases yesterday, in the relationship of the young woman to her mother. The relationship was described as symbiotic. My first question, would you have any particular observations on separation anxiety in the deaf? And my second question, are you aware of any school phobia, or history of school phobia, in the background of some of your case histories?

Dr. Altshuler:

Let me take up the second question first. I have seen a couple of school phobias developing, but they were usually an end response to a particular fear of the school, or a constellation of events at home, which were easily enough modified, so that the children were happy to come back to school. As for separation anxiety, that I have not seen.

Dr. Rainer:

Characteristically, there would not be much separation anxiety. It would be diminished because of the fact that there hasn't been that much closeness to separate from.

Dr. Altshuler:

We had contact with someone who has been a longtime worker with the deaf, and she told us that she saw a curious lack of prolonged grief or mourning at a loss, such as a death—which, of course, involves a clear and real separation.

Dr. Levy:

I was curious about the idea of loss of erotization of the ear zone in the course of development, and I am wondering whether or not we might theorize that this is displaced to the visual function, and that as a consequence, the visual apparatus becomes so much more important for the deaf person that one might perhaps expect to see in disorders of the deaf a greater incidence of such things as Peeping Toms or other antisocial problems, which present a practical problem in an outpatient setting. Have you come upon this as such?

Dr. Altshuler:

No, we have not. In our experience here we have not seen any particular increase of symptoms which you would refer to the eye. For the most part, we see mainly symptoms that one would refer to action impulse, shortsighted activities, not psychopathic—in the sense of some smooth swindler—but just impulsive actions, where a person does something destructive; he wants something, he steals it, and he is genuinely sorry afterwards, but he would do it again next time just the same.

It is an interesting point in the sense that this kind of theoretical construction can be tested by collecting developmental material. This is one of the things we really need to do so much more in psychiatric research, but unfortunately, it is seldom done.

Dr. Shipley:

I understand that loneliness often is a psychopathological stress point among the deaf, even in deaf schools. At least, that is what I am told by some of the teachers in our school. Would you care to comment about this as a psychological determinant?

Dr. Rainer:

I wonder what the experience along these lines is, of some of you people who have had contact with the deaf. I have certainly seen in deaf adolescents complaints of terrific loneliness. They can't communicate; they can't use the telephone. They feel very sad and lonely.

Dr. Shipley:

The point of my question is, is it enough of a factor so that one can make a generalization to the effect that the deaf, by and large, suffer from loneliness.

Dr. Adams:

This reminds me of what happens in the book by Carson McCullers, *The Heart is a Lonely Hunter*. The central character, who plays a most meaningful role, is a deaf mute who finally commits suicide, whereupon they all realize that he was tremendously lonely, and that he was not by any means the understanding, empathetic person they had thought him all along.

Dr. Altshuler:

I would say a problem arises, when you try to ask if the deaf are more, or less lonely than other people. For it is hard to measure loneliness.

The fact is that deaf people tend to congregate and cluster in the cities near their schools; they maintain a lot of contact with the school, and they often use the school as a base to return to when they are in trouble, to check back in with, the way this fellow whom we showed you yesterday uses our hospital.

The schools are places where the deaf seem to feel understood and communicated with and cared for. There are other deaf people, of course, who are perhaps even more alone, but I don't know how one could make a comparison of the more or the less lonely.

Dr. Vollenweider:

It has been the feeling of several of us who work with the deaf that they like to be with people. I think that withdrawal is a symptom that is frequently seen among hearing schizophrenics. The deaf don't seem to lose that drive to be with people. It probably is a compensation for the loneliness that they are made to feel. They get gratification out of it.

Dr. Altshuler:

In this connection, it seems to me that we look at deaf people and conclude, "They don't hear. They must be isolated."

They are isolated, to be sure, but whether they feel isolated is a different matter. We have to be careful that we are not reading into them what we would feel if we were in their position. They may, because of the absence of audition, have an entirely different experience, one not perceived with the emotional qualities that we think of when we speak of isolation.

Question:

I think this draws attention to the essence of communication, where it is often not the intellectualized inclination or the verbal information that seems to be important.

It has frequently been my experience, in talking to deaf people, that they will make some gesture that indicates understanding or affirmation of what has been said. When you follow it up, however, with some kind of interrogation or interrogatory remark to see if this is true, you find that it is not true. This seems to indicate that the important thing is that there have been two people, that there has been an affective diad, but that the understanding of content is sort of a fringe benefit. One gets the sense that the experience is gratifying; people are smiling. The deaf man grins and nods, but the information that you think you are conveying, that your attention is focused on, may be totally misunderstood by the other.

Dr. Altshuler:

Yes, that can certainly occur.

Diagnostic Considerations in Psychiatric Work With the Deaf

Psychiatric Examination

Dr. John D. Rainer

Dr. Rainer:

I would like to turn now to some of the diagnostic problems, a few of which you saw in action yesterday.

Diagnosis can be approached in two ways; first, in terms of phenomenon and symptom diagnosis and secondly, and in more dynamic terms, as developmental diagnosis, development of personality traits, both normal and pathological.

For example, starting with the psychosis, schizophrenia; Dr. Altshuler spoke about the expectancy of schizophrenia in the deaf, which may be slightly but not tremendously higher than it is among the hearing. It may even not be any higher at all, because of the greater length of time that the patients stay in the hospital, and also because some of the work that we and others are doing with the hearing in schizophrenia seems to indicate that probably the expectancy of schizophrenia in the hearing population, is greater than the 1 percent figure which is so commonly used; so the two may be closer together than is generally thought.

Psychiatrists who have had little contact with the deaf sometimes, at first blush, call almost any deaf adult patient who comes in schizophrenic, on the basis of what seems to be the fragmented language and the poor grammar and the concreteness.

It took us a few years, actually, to be able to distinguish the associative disorders, the thinking disorders in the deaf which are schizophrenic in nature, from the concreteness and grammatical difficulties which have to do with the hearing loss.

It was also difficult to distinguish inappropriate emotional tone or shallowness of emotional tone, both of which are typical of schizophrenia, from some of the empathic difficulties we have already referred to, that is, difficulties in appreciating and communicating feelings between two people.

85

Using the examiner as a tool, I have found that one criterion that has frequently served, in this differential diagnosis, is the understanding by the deaf patient that he is being interviewed by, and is talking to, a hearing psychiatrist whose proficiency in the sign language (if this is what is being used) is not as great as his.

The ability of the deaf patient to gauge his communication to the skills of the person who is interviewing him, is a useful measure of his social empathy and his insight.

A healthy sense of time and place orientation is shown when a patient says, "How did you learn the sign language," and "Am I speaking too fast?" Sometimes when I begin to doubt my ability to read back the sign language with many of the patients that come, I am reassured when communicating with good, healthy deaf persons who are able to sign very well, but are signing to me. They know that they are signing in a way that I, a hearing person—relatively unschooled in the sign language—can understand. They don't sign that way when they sign to deaf people who are much better at sign language. When they sign to me, they know to whom they are signing. This is a feeling for and an awareness of the listener, which has served as a rule-of-thumb diagnostic criterion, particularly, in respect to some of the inappropriateness that goes with schizophrenia.

We have noticed that some of the more regressed deaf schizophrenic patients will simply repeat in signs what you sign to them, a kind of echo phenomenon. They seem to be concerned with repetition, of the same phrase, of the same question, and sometimes, in their recollections, they repeat the same story again and again; something that happened at one time in their life. They keep repeating it like the girl we saw yesterday, for whom certain words were a constant source of repetition.

Delusions and hallucinations have been mentioned in our discussions. Paranoid delusions are present in the deaf, but they are not strikingly more common in the deaf than in the hearing.

The question of auditory hallucinations is an interesting one, and not fully worked out. As for other psychotic illnesses, Dr. Altshuler has pointed out that agitated depression is found among the deaf, including involutional depression, but the symptoms of retarded depression are less often seen.

There is still another thing about the diagnosis of schizophrenia, and that is that we have had to rely on the behavior and the bizarre actions, rather than on the language or the speech.

In the nonpsychotic disorders, you actually saw examples of most of these yesterday. You saw what we called the primitive personality, specifically the girl who was hospitalized with her mother—the immaturity or the inexperience—with the immaturity being almost a characteristic of many deaf people and particularly of this group.

An example of the impulsive disorder, the unruly impulsive bizarre activity—was a young deaf patient of ours who would steal transistor radios. I don't know what he wanted with a transistor radio; we never found out why, but he would steal things and humbly confess he had done so, and not know why he did it. He was like a psychopath but not with that suave, complete disregard of right and wrong. He knew he was wrong after he did it, but it did not stop him from doing it again.

If there is a conscience defect or superego defect, in some of these deaf patients, it seems to be different, perhaps, based on the timing of the development of the superego, on the types of controls, rather than on the complete absence of control.

These deaf patients with primitive personalities often show tantrums and subsequently they may turn around and be very friendly. They have accounted for a large percentage of the patients coming into our outpatient clinic. They show a lack of empathy and a lack of critical self awareness. I rather suspect this has something to do with the lack of affective interchange in the early days. It has to be differentiated from the impulsive disorder that comes with mental defect or with organic defect. Certainly, we must not overlook this difference.

My presentation, I think, is colored by the fact that we started our work with the deaf with adults. Historically, we started with the adult syndromes, and have worked our way back, you might say, to the adolescents, and then to the younger deaf patients, where the differentiation from organic defect and between brain damage, aphasia and deafness is important.

In the adolescent we see primary behavior disorders and situational adjustment problems. In the adult, aside from the psychotic disorders, we do not see so much of the classical neurotic syndrome, such as the obsessional. I think I have come upon no more than one classical handwashing neurosis. We don't see the classical neuroses. This difference probably has to do with the symbolization process. Possibly the classical neuroses as they have been described, and as we see them in the hearing, have something to do with the symbolization of anxiety.

If neurosis is a defense against anxiety, what is the anxiety that the deaf person experiences in the early years? Perhaps it is different from the anxiety in the hearing. One would expect the overwhelming type of anxiety that he might experience would override the types of anxiety that one sees in the general population, such as castration anxiety, for example. His anxiety may be symbolized in different ways.

One deaf patient I treated, in a dream pictured the loneliness, the lack of appreciation of symbols and of sound which occurred in his family. He was a boy who was interested in playing baseball. I was interested to see the boy again yesterday in one of the classrooms we visited. He seems to be doing well. This boy dreamt that he was in a dark baseball stadium, all dark, and the stands were completely dark. He could see nothing. He was the catcher behind the plate, and these balls were coming toward him, but they weren't ordinary balls, they were ectoplasmic swirls of smoke. Each time the balls hit his glove they would drop down and he would miss catching them. Everything was dark and he couldn't see what was going on out there.

When I asked him to tell me more about the dream, he simply repeated the description of it. As I pressed him to tell more, he complained, "We deaf people are dumb, stupid. You can't expect me to tell more about the dream. I don't understand what you're asking me." It was then possible to tell him, "This is precisely what your dream is about. You see but you don't understand. You think you are stupid. You see words and people's lips, but they are ghostly and fuzzy, and it is as though they were coming toward you from a darkness; you can't catch them." This boy's hearing family was not very geared to communicating with him.

This is a type of anxiety where there is loneliness. The loneliness may be defended against at different times in a way that is different from defenses against the anxieties which other children face. The timetable may differ, and the emotional reactions may differ, the rage and anxiety may differ in their quality and in their timing. Different things may be defended against, so that one gets different personality structures and different diagnostic descriptions.

Psychological Testing

Dr. John A. Vollenweider

Dr. Rainer:

The psychologist is in a good position to pick out some of the sources of anxiety, of these distortions in thinking, and also some of the body-image defects, and the self-image defects which I have not especially mentioned, but which are prominent in the deaf.

The next speaker, therefore, is Dr. John Vollenweider, who has been doing a good deal of work over the past years in psychological testing of our deaf patients. He has also written a chapter in our recent book [1] on the role of the psychologist, with particular emphasis on the use of the Rorschach test. This chapter is in the classical tradition of Dr. Edna Levine's work with the Rorschach in the normal deaf. Dr. Vollenweider has also utilized figure drawings in tests of organicity as well as intelligence. He can, perhaps, tell us something about what psychological testing can contribute to this very difficult problem in which we are now only beginning to fathom the developmental and phenomenological diagnosis of neurotic and psychotic behavior disorders of the deaf of various ages.

Dr. Vollenweider:

In the unit for the deaf my two major functions are psychological testing and psychotherapy. In this talk I am focusing upon psychological testing.

As with hearing subjects, the primary purposes in testing deaf patients are (1) to obtain information which is useful in establishing diagnoses and prognoses, and in determining the significant levels or significant areas to be dealt with in treatment, (2) to obtain information which would aid in vocational and educational planning, and of course, (3) to evaluate the current intellectual functioning of the patient, and gain some insight about whether this may represent a marked decline in his intellectual capacity, i.e., whether the illness has seriously impaired intellectual function.

I came into the project in 1963, and like most of the other staff members in the newly established unit for the deaf at Rockland State Hospital, I had no prior experience in working with the deaf.

In selecting tests for use with our patients, I relied heavily on the recommendations of Dr. Edna Levine, and other psychologists with extensive experience in this area. On the basis of these recommendations, I decided it would be fitting to use the Wechsler Intelligence Scales to evaluate intelligence, the Bender Gestalt to test for organicity and perceptual-motor functioning, and certain projective personality tests, such as the TAT, Rorschach, and the human figure drawings.

In testing a deaf patient, the extent of the test battery that I use is almost entirely dependent upon his ability to communicate. That is

[1] Rainer, J. D. and Altshuler, K. Z. *Comprehensive Mental Health Services for the Deaf.* New York State Psychiatric Institute. 1966.

the major factor which sets limits on how many tests I will give. Contrary to what one might expect with disturbed deaf psychiatric patients, refusal or resistance to testing is not often a problem. As a matter of fact, I think that deaf psychiatric patients are as cooperative, or possibly even more cooperative than hearing psychiatric patients.

I also found the deaf to be a very tolerant, patient group. For a long time I had a great deal of difficulty with the sign language, and I would often have to ask patients to repeat and repeat what they had communicated. It was only a rare occasion when one of them would show any irritability.

In administering tests, the mode of communication I use is also determined by the patients' communication skills. Among all the patients I have tested, a few were such competent oralists and lipreaders that all directions and explanations could be given orally. With the vast majority of patients, simultaneous speech and signing proved the most effective approach. A few patients were so lacking in any conventional communication skill, that reliance had to be placed on pantomime.

Regardless of which mode of communication was used, it soon became obvious, as it has to any psychologist who has worked with the deaf, that a great deal of caution had to be exercised to insure that a patient understands what is expected of him. If pains are not taken to insure comprehension, the danger of faulty interpretation of test responses is great. For example, on tests sampling capacity for verbal reasoning and judgment, a deaf person can give responses which are extremely irrelevant, tangential, and seemingly confused. Such responses could easily be misinterpreted as indicating pathological disturbance in thinking, whereas, in reality, they are merely the result of faulty comprehension.

Certain modifications of standard testing procedures are used to insure comprehension. Instructions are simplified and test questions are rephrased using language and concepts with which the deaf are familiar. Levine made such an adaptation of the Wechsler Verbal test items, being careful not to change the difficulty level of test items. Another modification of standard testing procedure is that far greater emphasis is placed on demonstration of test materials than is the case when working with hearing patients.

The test battery which I have described has both merits and limitations. I have already mentioned one of the major limitations, namely, that quite often it is not possible to use very rewarding tests such as the Rorschach and TAT because of a patients' poor communication skill. Another factor which detracts from the usefulness of these tests is that the majority of patients I've given them to were very underproductive on these tests. On the Rorschach, for example, the average number of responses given by hearing subjects is about 25 while that of our deaf schizophrenic was 18. Furthermore, elaboration of Rorschach responses is usually minimal. On the TAT, the stories elicited from deaf patients are more like descriptions of the pictures, rather than interpretations of them. Both the qualitative and quantitative limitations of the patients' responses to the projective tests limit the usefulness of the tests for achieving comprehensive pictures of personality structure.

Another major limitation of the battery is that all of the tests were developed and standardized with hearing subjects. Very few tests have been designed specifically for use with the deaf.

While it is true that many studies have been done with the deaf employing these tests, the vast majority suffer from such marked limitations in scope and design that the reported findings cannot serve as normative data. Therefore, the psychologist has no alternative but to use tests designed for the hearing, keeping in mind that blind use of hearing norms to evaluate test performance of deaf patients would be foolhardy and misleading. In the absence of adequate normative data, great care must be exercised in deciding to what extent deviations in performance represent pathology, or are the natural consequences of deafness, limited language facility, scholastic background, and the like.

In spite of these major shortcomings of the test battery, it has proved useful in a number of important respects. The battery, together with close observations of the patient during testing, usually yields a reasonably valid assessment of intellectual functioning and capacity, major personality traits, adequacy of controls, diagnosis and prognosis. Support for the validity of test-based inferences came from their high concordance with independent psychiatric judgments and from observation of the patients over a long period of time.

I will now like to say a few words about the Rorschach performance of 22 deaf schizophrenics I examined between 1963 and 1966. I want to stress that this sample of schizophrenics is both selected and heterogeneous and that generalization drawn from the test data must be limited. The data cannot be taken as normative but they do at least provide a descriptive portrait of the patient group on which they are based. They also provide leads and hypothesis for systematic research at a future date, once a sufficient number of Rorschach protocols are collected.

I wanted to have some idea of the performance of normal deaf subjects on the Rorschach for purposes of comparison. In searching the literature I was only able to find a few studies. Of these, the best was a well designed investigation by Levine [2] who used a carefully selected group of 31 normal deaf adolescent females. Comparison of the Rorschach data of Levine's normal subjects with those of the schizophrenic subjects revealed a number of significant differences.

On the average, the normal deaf subject produces as many responses as does the average hearing subject. The average productivity of the schizophrenic, on the other hand, was considerably lower. This limited productivity probably stemmed from blocking, poverty of associational content, lack of flexibility, limitations in adaptability to new situations, and impairment of capacity for differential perception and abstractions.

A second major difference between the groups was that Levine's subjects showed a tendency to respond primarily to the obvious, major subdivisions of a blot, while being relatively unresponsive to the blot taken as a whole. Exactly the opposite tendency was observed in the schizophrenic group. This finding, together with qualitative aspects of the responses, indicated that the perception of deaf schizophrenics has a global, undifferentiated quality, while that of the normal deaf subjects reflects a tendency toward concreteness and a need to cling to what is familiar and obvious.

Another significant difference suggested by intergroup comparison is that the schizophrenics guard against uncertainty by restricting their attention to inconsequential, minute aspects of their environment. The normals did not show this behavior.

Differences related to capacity for reality testing and emotional responsiveness were in the expected directions—the normals showing considerably greater objectivity and capacity for relatedness.

In closing, I again want to stress that the Rorschach findings I have reported are based on a small, very heterogeneous sample of schizophrenics. The findings are not intended as normative data. Their main value is that they indicate that the Rorschach may be used with deaf psychotics, and that from such productive clinical application, hypotheses may be derived which can be tested systematically in the future.

Dr. Rainer:

What about tests for organicity? Are these valid?

---

[2] Levine, E. S. *Youth in a Soundless World*, New York, N.Y. University Press, 1956.

Dr. Vollenweider:

I used the Bender Gestalt test, as a test of perceptual motor development, and also to evaluate organicity. It is quite a good test for determining this. I use this to supplement the findings of the Wechsler-Bellevue scales and the Rorschach, which also may or may not suggest organicity.

Dr. Boston:

Were the Wechsler and Bender normal?

Dr. Vollenweider:

The Benders were very interesting in terms of something that someone else said before; namely, that the deaf were compensating with vision for the absence of hearing. The average deaf patient seems to have better recall of Bender designs than his hearing counterpart. Quite a few patients will not only recall the Benders exactly, but they will also reproduce them in the order that they originally were presented. Their immediate recall of the designs is, I would say, superior to that of hearing adults.

In the Bender, they have a design in front of them when they first reproduce it. But at the end I take the design away, wait 10 seconds, and then have them reproduce it from memory.

I find they do pretty well on both. They do about average on the reproduction, but very well on the recall.

Another interesting thing I found, using the Rorschach, is that the deaf schizophrenics do not produce extremely disturbed responses as do the hearing patients. They don't have the gory, the very florid quality of the Rorschachs of many hearing schizophrenics. That was an interesting finding.

Dr. Adams:

What about the drawing of the human figure? Is that as disturbed with adult deaf as it is with child deaf?

Dr. Vollenweider:

I routinely give figure drawings.

Dr. Adams:

With deaf children, one of our psychologists found that there is a tremendous disturbance in body image and in the capacity to visualize the human figure as an intact, integrated unit.

Dr. Vollenweider:

Particularly with schizophrenics and organics, of course.

Dr. Adams:

Do adult deaf show disturbance in body image?

Dr. Vollenweider:

Yes, they often do.

Dr. Levy:

Do we have a standardized group of drawings from nonpsychotic deaf to be compared with those of the psychotic deaf?

Dr. Vollenweider:

That is precisely what we need. I understand that some psychologists are accumulating this kind of drawing for that very purpose.

Dr. Levy:

Do you ever administer animal drawings? Do you ask your patients to draw animals?

Dr. Vollenweider:

No, I haven't used them.

Group Therapy

Dr. M. Bruce Sarlin

Dr. Rainer:

We need every tool we can get. This afternoon we are going to turn
to the problems of treatment and therapy. We hope to hear more from
some of you who have been doing therapy individually and in groups
with the deaf.

Now we will end our morning program with a discussion of the
group therapy or group discussion sessions with the deaf students at
the New York School for the Deaf. We have a television tape and a
discussion by Dr. Sarlin.

Dr. Sarlin:

This paper and audiovisual presentation represent some observations and a progress report of a preventive group psychotherapy program with deaf adolescents. The subjects were students at the New
York School for the Deaf, White Plains, N.Y. The student population, composed of 277 children from 3½ to 19 years of age, receive a
special education geared to the handicap of early total deafness. As
you have already heard, the students come mainly from the New York
City metropolitan area or nearby suburban counties; most reside at
the school and return home only on weekends.

A striking feature of our early findings with the deaf students was
a widespread lack of group cohesiveness. With a group of 10–12-
year-old boys, this appeared to inhibit and prevent them from establishing an effective therapeutic alliance, with the boys remaining
seven individuals clamoring for the doctor's attention. Among two
groups of older students (boys 13–16 years and girls 13–15 years)
there appeared to be a considerable lag in the development of a codified, accurate knowledge of sexual reproductive function, despite considerable interest and active experimentation among the students,
although the girls showed some concern with their future roles as wife
and mother. A preoccupation with violence and retaliation was also
notable among the boys.

95

To extend these findings, we set out to determine how a representative, undiagnosed group of students at the school would compare with the previously observed groups. We chose a study hall class of 15- and 16-year-old students consisting of 5 boys and 4 girls, most of whom attended classes together. We felt that this already existing somewhat cohesive group might enhance our therapeutic efforts. Our goals for the study were, first, to explore the group's potential for interaction with each other, to encourage them in developing group feelings and responsibilities, to elicit any common preoccupations or concerns, to determine any sex-specific differences in these areas, and finally, to detect and treat any incipient signs of emotional disorder.

Meeting once a week since October 1966, the student group has gradually welded itself into a working therapeutic team in alliance with the therapist. Communication has been carried on by all available modalities, including speech and the manual language. The course of the group has not been smooth or without complications, and the group has passed through several difficult stages along the way.

The first session was attended by Mrs. Minor, the school psychologist, myself and Dr. Rainer, who supervised and guided the therapeutic team in the turbulent sessions during the first half of the academic year. Subsequently Dr. Altshuler has been supervising the group, mostly with the use of taped recordings, as well as with notes made in retrospect, immediately following the group sessions.

Initially, considerable interest and suspiciousness was expressed regarding the reasons for the specific study hall group chosen. There were a number of fears expressed, and some trepidation, which eventually became intermingled with a certain pleasure over the exclusiveness of the students' relationship with the therapist. Considerable testing ensued during the early sessions, with the students offering many questions regarding intellectual, metaphysical, and religious matters, and with each student attempting to involve the therapist in a diadic relationship to the exclusion of the others in the group.

Perhaps partly in response to the therapist's efforts to avoid such exclusive relationships, several students in the fourth session began voicing complaints that the school was doing very little for them, and they contemplated leaving school to get a job. At this point the barriers between the students began to break down, with several individuals expressing a lot of feeling about the values and benefits of a completed education, and the advisability of remaining in school. Those students who had been silent heretofore began to share their feelings in an active discussion. The potential dropouts were dramatically admonished, and there were even hints of a wish for continued friendship.

It is notable that most of the reasons offered for remaining in school were based on emotional factors, with little rational basis. The idea seemed to be that school is good because it is supposed to be good, and it is also legally required. Through these discussions, the general axiom of "school is good" gave way to in-depth explorations of how school was good, for what type of job it may be helpful, and how school now might better prepare one for life by providing the specific skills necessary to insure one's future security. Subsequently the students have expressed greater ease in sharing their thoughts and feelings with one another, the occasional feelings of accomplishment, more frequent experiences of failure, and the numerous frustrations experienced along the way in their strivings for feelings of mastery.

The use of dreams in group therapy has been found to be a valuable technique by several experienced workers.[1, 2] Occasional patients with early total deafness in individual therapy have profited from interpretation of dream material.[3] With the hospitalized mentally ill deaf, dreams were noted to be helpful in alerting the therapist to the underlying conflicts but less helpful in the therapy itself.[4]

With the present group of students, only one dream has been presented for discussion. The dream was brought out in a session which was videotaped for presentation to this conference. One week before, the students were informed that a demonstration film was to be made, depicting one of our projects at the school. The intended use of the film was fully explained, and the students were requested to dress appropriately (e.g., blue shirts for the boys). The day of the taping, the discussion began with questions about how the audience would understand what was transpiring. Then Jacob, the manager of the football team and an aspiring youngster, related the following dream which he recalled from the night before.

I was at a party with a hearing girl. I began to dance with the girl, and suddenly I was interrupted by another boy. He took the girl away from me and I found myself standing in the middle of the dance floor, feeling all alone and sad.

Jacob felt at a loss to elaborate or explore his feelings about the dream, and the group dealt with it in a very concrete way. The fol-

[1] Slavson, S. P. *A Textbook in Analytic Group Psychotherapy.* New York, International Universities Press, 1964.
[2] Wolf, A. and Schwartz, E. K. *Psychoanalysis in Groups.* New York, Grune & Stratton, 1962.
[3] Rainer, J. D., Altshuler, K. Z. and Kallmann, F. J. Psychotherapy for the deaf. *Adv. Psychosom. Med., 3:* 167–179, 1963.
[4] Rainer, J. D. and Altshuler, K. Z. *Comprehensive Mental Health Services for the Deaf.* New York, New York State Psychiatric Institute, 1966.

lowing is a running dialogue of a portion of the videotape immediately following the recounting of the dream:

(The videotaped session was shown. It included the opening discussion and the dream already noted, the following dialogue, and a good deal of exchange on the part of the students. It also served to demonstrate the mixture of oralism and manual language used in communication, and some of the concreteness and disinterest alternating with more active involvement with each other which it is the therapist's task to encourage and explore. The repetition on the part of the therapist is helpful in rephrasing as he signs, and serves to insure understanding.)

Therapist:

I think I understand. What do you think the dream means? Why **would you have a dream of someone fighting with you and interrupting you?** Why would you have a dream like that? * * * No idea, well, do you have any other thoughts about the dream?

Milton:

Maybe it has to do with wishes for the future.

Therapist:

Usually, dreams pertain to something that happened the day before which we dream about at night. Sometimes they have to do with what we expect to happen the next day. I would like to know what the other people in the group think about this dream. Do any of you have any thoughts about Jacob's dream? Does anyone have an idea of what his dream means? Let me see if I understand your dream, okay? You were at a party and you were dancing with a girl, right, and someone came up to you and hit you, took your girl away, is that right? Is that part of the dream?

Jacob:

Yes.

Therapist:

Does anyone have an idea why Jacob would see himself dancing with a girl and someone going up to him and hitting him and taking his girl away? Sometimes hopes and wishes come up in dreams. In your dream everything good seemed to occur. You were at a party, dancing with a girl, then why should you have someone interrupt? Would anyone like to guess? I have an idea, but I would like to give the others a chance to give their ideas.

Milton:

Maybe the boy saw that he was not a good dancer.

Mary:

Jealous. Do you think the boy who interrupted him was jealous?

Therapist:

Perhaps seeing Jacob dance with a nice girl made the other boy feel jealous.

Milton:

Maybe the girl danced with the other boy because she felt that he isn't important.

Therapist (putting into words what one of the other students had signed):

Mary thought that the other boy felt that Jacob was very important and interrupted him because of that.

(An interpretation of the dream was offered at this point by the therapist, using the general idea that Jacob did not seem to feel he would come off well showing himself in competition with others. Perhaps he felt that such pleasure was wrong and therefore punishable. There ensued some attempt at clarifying the distortion of Jacob's percepts by the therapist and the group. The underlying idea, that Jacob's dream was probably evoked in anticipation of the taping and showed his wish and fear of competitive exhibitionism was not touched upon, for it seemed to involve a series of abstract steps that could not be made meaningful to the boy or the group at this stage.)

In summary, our experience at the New York School for the Deaf suggests that group psychotherapy may well be an effective research tool and treatment modality for deaf adolescents when used by a therapist trained in communication with the deaf as well as in dynamic psychiatry. An accidental finding was that the use of the audio-visual equipment proved to be valuable in provoking a conflict which brought out the only dream so far presented by the group. The dream heightened the insight of the therapist into the nature of the individual dynamics and was helpful in focusing the group's attention on emotions and the fact they exist and guide our actions though they are not always visible. Problems encountered during the course of this group experiment included the need for the therapist to be alert to specific maturational lags and experiential naivete, and to concretize abstract concepts so that interpretation of behavior and fantasy could be made more meaningful to these cognitively impaired youngsters.

Discussion

Dr. Rainer:

Are there any questions or comments?

Dr. Paltrow:

At the school for the deaf in Salem, Oreg., I had several normal, hard-of-hearing, teenage youngsters, and I noticed that when they used the oral method with each other without sign language, they had much more difficulty understanding each other than when hearing people spoke to them.

Dr. Sarlin:

I can confirm your observation. The fact that both modalities of communication are utilized does, I think, enhance the effectiveness of the group interaction.

Question:

I noticed three of the young girls wearing ties. Has this anything to do with fashion or identification?

Dr. Sarlin:

There seemed to be a lot of attention to the fact that we encouraged the girls and boys to wear blue, because it shows up best on television. Perhaps this was interpreted, or misinterpreted, as some need for them to conform to my expectations, and so they came wearing blue ties and white shirts. That has come up during several other sessions, where there has been much interest and discussion of fashion and clothing, subjects that adolescents are normally concerned with.

For example, on the day prior to the Easter vacation there was a fashion show in the auditorium, scheduled at the same time as group session. Three of the girls and one of the boys got up, left the group, and went into the auditorium. They stated that they were interested in seeing the fashion show, despite the therapist's encouragement to stay. After the fashion show was over in the auditorium they returned to the group, stating merely that the show was brief and that they were now able to return. During the time that part of the group was away at the fashion show, Jacob became furious. The conflict between his loyalty, or staying in the room to please the therapist, and his wish to see the fashion show himself appeared to be the issue. But in general, the students are very much concerned about clothing and what is the vogue and the style.

Question:

It seems to me that it is hard enough for those people to express themselves in the first place, as the boy did when he kept asking why he would be hit by another boy. But, when the answer was that he is unimportant, a girl said that maybe he is important. It seemed to me he gave up more readily than anybody else would have done. Can you draw any generalization from that?

Dr. Sarlin:

You say he gave up more readily?

Question:

It seemed to me he struggled to come out with a feeling, in the first place, about the boy in the dream. He tried hard to get it out. Once it was gotten out and it didn't seem to fit, he gave up. Perhaps he might have pursued his point or argued with you, or argued with the other girl.

Dr. Sarlin:

It is interesting that you noticed that. I'm not sure if he gave up or just withdrew without much interest. One of the things I've found necessary to do is to encourage the students to interact with one another, and at the same time I try to find a balance between intruding too much myself and allowing them to go on by themselves. I think it is therapeutic for us to try to heighten the interaction among the group, but with adolescents the therapist must be somewhat more active than in working with adults.

Dr. Rainer:

Do you think that deaf people give up more or less than hearing people? The tendency to give up and to say, "I am stupid," that type of response is strong. We have noted it frequently.

Question:

On the matter of psychotherapy, I wondered how much was a function of the problems of the deaf in group psychotherapy.

Dr. Rainer:

Dr. Robinson may have some comments at this point, with regard to the interaction.

Dr. Robinson:

I think it depends on how much the therapist would encourage the person to continue talking about this, or if the person would gather from the therapist that he must stop because the therapist is challenging him. That is something else.

Dr. Sarlin:

Perhaps I felt I had to come to the support of the boy who had the dream. When one of the other boys said, in effect, "you aren't important, and you don't know how to dance," I felt that these were unfair rebukes. Jacob had presented a good dream, and I felt it was inappropriate for him to be so severely rebuffed. So, in the absence of any other support of him, I chimed in with "maybe the others feel that he is very important."

Dr. Rainer:

The fact that he can produce a wonderful dream doesn't make him feel that he is a worthwhile person. It is like the baseball dream that I mentioned before. The more you ask him to tell about the dream, the more he becomes aware that he is stupid or can't catch. Techniques have to be developed to get deaf people to talk about their dreams or experiences.

Dr. Grinker:

I would take a different point of view. As a matter of fact, I felt that in individual psychotherapy or in group psychotherapy, whether it be deaf or any kind or group of person, the use of dream material represents a breakdown in the therapeutic process.

The dream is difficult enough to remember. Its manifest content should be accepted, I believe, like any other communication. To call for associations is something that impresses people, whether in individual or in group therapy, with the importance attributed to it. It has a tendency to stimulate the memory and the use of dreams and bringing them to therapy.

I cannot see that it adds anything till you can see some connection to the manifest content. Then the dream is fine. But to try to get associations and to try to analyze the preconscious and unconscious elements of the dream, I think is not part of technical procedures that are valuable, so far as therapy is concerned.

I believe, and I will come back to the subject this afternoon, that there is premature application of psychoanalytic theory to the problems of the deaf. I think that we are still in the process of developing hypotheses, and when one attempts to transfer psychoanalytic theory to whatever one is engaged in, especially group therapy, I think this is premature. I consider it a breakdown of group therapy.

Dr. Altshuler:

In this group it has been very unusual for us to have this kind of dream reporting. It may have well been in some sense a function of the television camera.

The young members in this session were quite different from what they were in many of the other groups. Even their attitude toward dress, I think, was much more heightened. One of the things that probably struck Dr. Sarlin about this was not so much the use of the dream for its therapeutic value, but an attempt to understand some of the ideas of symbolization in the dreams of the deaf.

There is only one study that has paid attention to symbolization in dreams of the deaf. College students were surveyed, somewhat superficially I believe, and the essence of the results was that the more highly-motivated material in the dreams was portrayed in either sign language or just felt by the subject in the dream, while the more civilized, the more sophisticated aspects of interchange were portrayed in lipreading or finger spelling; I believe this was the way it was put.

There are many ways in which you can approach the symbolic processes of the dreams. I think that the dreams of the deaf are a handle for getting into that. Dreams would tell us something more about how the cognitive process works, or it may even lead to defining, perhaps, a different process of integration.

Participant:

If there is a relationship between the content of the drawings, at least of adolescent deaf children, and the kind of dream reporting, it may be because of the lack of symbolic skills and sophisticated language function; the dreams are curiously undeveloped.

This seems to be the case with the drawings that these youngsters produce. There is a lack of, or bareness of social propriety, and sometimes a dynamic picture in the drawing seems to be not adequately developed, or to have the same symbolic representation that would be found in the hearing. It is almost a pictograph kind of abbreviation of reality, but not really a highly symbolic one. This might have some implications as to the kind of work that is done therapeutically with dream material.

Dr. Sarlin:

I think that the manifest part of the dream may very well mask the wish. I think the dream presented was a very sophisticated one. Unfortunately, we didn't get a chance to see the dream as he further elaborates on it. But he did say that the concept is a very difficult one for him to get across to us.

This boy is one who has a great deal of conceptual skill and ability. I think we have to try our very best to understand what is going on with these patients and to help them with their concerns. Certainly one of the things we must find out is how they are similar and how they are different from hearing adolescents, and what the areas of mutuality and the areas of difference are.

Dr. Levy:

I would like to ask those of you who do work with adolescent and adult mentally disturbed deaf whether dreams appear to come up more frequently, or are introduced by patients, more often than among those who are not deaf?

Dr. Abdullah:

Spontaneously, they do not come up. A few times I have tried to introduce the subject in the group. The result was very simple dreams, very nonsymbolic, such as a girl who was borderline mentally defective seeing herself getting married.

So far there has been nothing much in the way of dreams reported by the psychotic group. I try, sometimes, to see if there is anything we can do with the dreams, but felt I was wasting a lot of time. I found we were better off on more concrete experiential and intuitive approaches than on this symbolic one. My point is that it seemed to confuse them.

Dr. Robinson:

I have been working with group psychotherapy for about 3 years, and so far no group member has related a dream. One has expressed an elaborate system of auditory hallucinations, but she has done this only twice in the group over a period of 3 years. In individual therapy, the same patient will bring up her own auditory hallucinations almost every session, but not in the group.

Psychiatric Treatment of the Deaf

Dr. Syed Abdullah

Dr. Altshuler:

You have already seen the inpatient unit and patients on it. Some of the therapeutic and group psychotherapeutic experiences and techniques have been touched upon. Building on these bases, Dr. Abdullah will tell you more about, and discuss his own conceptual framework for, the psychiatric treatment of some of the deaf.

Dr. Abdullah:

My talk concerns a concept and approach to the therapy of the deaf. It is my concept that the process of maturity in any individual, say in a normal hearing child, can be thought of as an ongoing process of conditioning, imprints, and all the other processes that lead to maturation of the emotional, intellectual, and social responses of that individual. In the case of the deaf we can conceive of certain gaps in this development, and certain distortions. (See fig. 3.) There will be certain areas of fuzzy development, not exactly the same as gaps, but representing, rather, nebulous or uncertain development. There will be areas where the responses have become a little distorted. There are other areas of development where there are appropriate responses, to be sure, but there is not enough reinforcement of these responses.

Even if the strategy of the therapy is determined with this as a backdrop, a great challenge still remains with each individual deaf patient. This real challenge is to understand in which areas of his personality these gaps occur, in which areas there are distortions in his responses, and in which areas they are just nebulous or where adequate responses, though present, are not sufficiently reinforced because of the nature of his sensory deficiency. Of course, it is most important of all to know in which areas his responses are intact and adaptive.

When we conceive of studying the deaf personality profile in depth, we have to attempt to understand it and all its endowments and deficiencies, and to proceed on the basis of this model. Without such knowledge, the treatment will remain ineffective. What, then, is the way to do this?

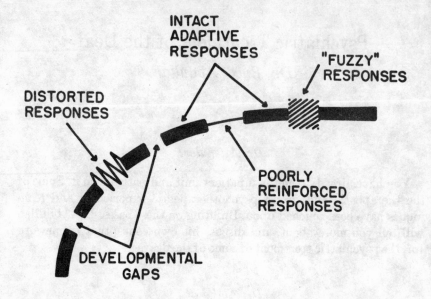

SCHEMA FOR CONCEPTUALIZING THE DEVELOP- MENT OF FAULTY ADAPTATION IN THE DEAF

FIGURE 3.

The best way, of course, is by very detailed history taking, to sit down and talk with the patient and to listen creatively. With prolonged periods of discussion these gaps and fulfillments, and the patient's spectrum of assets and shortcomings, become clearly delineated. Then we can perhaps go on, first of all, to working on his intact responses—that is, the adaptive responses which he has. Then we can pass on to the unreinforced or insufficiently reinforced responses, and try to build them up. Perhaps we may even attempt to do something about the many maladaptive responses which he has, depending on the capacity of the patient to go along. And perhaps we can do something about the developmental gaps. With patient and long drawn-out contacts in the hospital or outpatient clinic, or in the work situation in the community, we can sometimes bridge these gaps and make the individual function up to his optimal level.

This is the process which goes on when the patient comes to our ward. In the beginning, I used to be very frustrated in trying to understand the deaf. Of course, at that time this concept had not yet developed in my mind; the need arose and gave birth to the concept. For instance, a common feeling initially was that this patient understands what he wants to understand and does not understand what he doesn't want to understand. This might have been true at times. But sometimes it was due to the peculiar distortions in the patient's developmental processes as envisaged in the figure.

For example, it was mentioned yesterday in the case of one young man that he understands his mother's rejection, but he does not understand his grandmother's rejection because she wept when she turned him out of her house. He is confused about that. He is not conditioned to understand that two contradictory emotions can exist and act together in an individual.

In this connection, let me mention a personal incident. The other day my wife was doing some spring cleaning and she threw out a few things from the drawer. One of the things she discarded was a picture which my son, aged 6, had drawn. He watched her tear up the picture and throw it away. Then he approached his mother and asked, "Mummy, when I drew this picture you told me it was so cute. Then why did you just tear it up?"

I was sitting there and could not help but observe what happened. My wife took a long time to do the explaining. What she needed to do most, and what was most important, was to use a lot of warm, affectionate words, words of understanding, words meant to restore his confidence in her love. This process went on and on.

At once my mind switched to some of my deaf patients and I thought, specifically, of yesterday's patient and his confusion. He did not get this reinforcement, this proper conditioning of his response, that my son had received. I understood him a little better now.

It is very rewarding and fascinating to attempt to see what we can do with these glaring blanks. The other day one of our female patients came to my office and asked if kissing could cause pregnancy. She is 24 years old and she is not mentally retarded, yet there is an intellectual gap. We also have at this time a patient who is hospitalized because of his homosexual overtures towards children. He tells me that he has read in the Bible it is wrong to have sexual relationships outside marriage. This understanding of his is very clear. What is not clear to him is the difference in the nature of sexual relationship outside marriage, that between adults and that between an adult and a child, or between homo- and heterosexual relationships. I entered into discussion with him, trying to find out if he really had any preference for children over adults. He said that he didn't. It is okay with him if he has for his homosexual gratification a full-grown adult or a little child. But he says the child is easier to get. Then I asked, "Do you know the social implications of the difference?" And he said, "Yes, both are wrong."

We might dismiss all this as a statement of a psychopath, but the other possibility is also there, that in this particular individual, the social response and real awareness are not developed. It is not expected of a 24-year-old person in our society that he will bracket both sex offenses on the same level.

One day, a male patient threw a glass of orange juice at a nurse. When I asked, "Why did you do that?" he answered, "Well, John hit you. What is all the fuss about my hitting the nurse?"

In other words, these patients sometimes pick up isolated or fragmentary cues and their responses are distorted. It is a study in the conditioning of an individual. The correction of these distortions is a major effort in therapy. In the group sessions, of course, this process of conditioning goes on continuously. Actually, what we have done for the inpatients in our wards is to provide them with a milieu. They come, they interact and they start healing themselves. The significant thing is that they interact.

Of course, we control the milieu, which therefore becomes less amorphous. The patients interact, and they learn. They test out the living situation, the experience in social living. This actually is the psychotherapeutic approach. The potential to learn on the part of the patients is taken advantage of. Despite their age, some of them are behaving like adolescents and seem to be capable of acquiring imprints. If the appropriate imprint is offered to them, they do absorb it and their responses become more adaptive to their living situation.

We strive to utilize therapeutically everything that takes place on the ward. For instance, yesterday we had you gentlemen as our visitors. We used this for morale-lifting effect, as we have found it has such an influence on the patients. After you left, I spent some time with the patients on the ward and talked to them about this visit. They felt that they belonged to the greater community, and that people do have an interest in them. This feeling breeds an optimism and a tendency not to give up hope, and it motivates them to do what is to be done.

In summing up, let me mention the three most important things to which the deaf patient seems to respond positively. The first thing, I think, is *patience*. The deaf are very much used to impatience from hearing people. Most people are irked by the voice of the deaf, by their slowness of understanding, so patience has its own reward. The therapeutic process starts from the time the deaf patient can find patience in somebody who is willing to sit and listen.

The second thing is the question of *understanding*. I don't think I have to say anything further about understanding, because everyone, deaf or hearing, needs it.

The third thing to which they respond very positively is *compassion*. They are so much used to ridicule and that sort of thing that they almost immediately respond to compassion. And they are capable of responding very positively. A lot of work can be done through the process of compassion, a thing above pity.

Discussion

Dr. Vollenweider:

Would you like to say something about the success we have had with fluphenazine?

Dr. Abdullah:

We have used many drugs, and we have found that somehow our deaf patients have responded well, on the whole, to fluphenazine. But we are not in a position to make any sweeping statement on this.

Question:

Are you referring to hyperactivity?

Dr. Abdullah:

I am talking about the more withdrawn and delusional patients. In the beginning we did not use fluphenazine, we used trifluperazine. Fluphenazine seemed to activate these patients.

Question:

Are you able to bring hyperexcitable, very impulsive patients into that unit?

Dr. Abdullah:

Yes. We have had a great many impulsive patients. We sometimes use a heavy amount of chlorpromazine.

Question:

How much? What is the upper limit you have used?

Dr. Abdullah:

We have used chlorpromazine up to 250 mg q.i.d., plus i.m. doses when needed, but we try to cut it down as much as possible.

Dr. Grinker:

Dr. Abdullah asked me specially to discuss his presentation. First I would like to congratulate him on the general concept that he has developed. Next I would like to amplify it somewhat.

I think that what Dr. Abdullah has talked about here corresponds to what we utilized in general systems theory. He has portrayed the system of health and illness in an ontogenetic frame of reference. To split this up into significant parts of the whole system, we can envisage it in diagrammatic form.

In the first place, we know that there are genetic factors that must be taken into account for every kind of illness and for every quality of health. We know, also, that the environment is always interactive with the genetic background, and that this never loses its impact.

Let us begin with the primordial or the primitive organism, born into the world with a certain genetic disturbance or function, and the environment of a certain nature. It is said that 50 percent of the deaf have a genetic form of deafness. This might be, perhaps, a little higher than we expect, but certainly we know that either by birth or some time in early life there are influences which create disturbances in hearing.

The next phase can be described as one in which the organism with its genetic background is now subjected to environmental influences, particularly the mother-and-child relationship, and the parts of the organism are now composed of residuals of its experiences. In the case of early total deafness, one of these parts is not present, it is lacking. We now have a defect which persists.

Let us next assume a level which might be called proneness. There is no reversibility of proneness. The only people who would disagree with me on this point are those psychoanalysts who believe that the primary structure of the personality can be altered. You hear a good deal about reorganization of the personality, but I do not think it can go this far.

We next have a phase of sickness, the phase of chronicity of sickness; this is reversible in either sex. Then come the processes of aging, death and dying—there is no reversibility of aging.

An infant lying flat at last staggers up on its feet, upright, and in the upright position maintains a plateau to middle age. It then begins to stoop over and move downward, until, finally, gravity wins out again as he is placed on the ground.

If we view the subsystems of the system of health and illness in these ontogenetic phases, then we can observe the kind of interferences that are feasible in prevention and therapy, and we will not expect more than can be applied at any particular phase of the system.

For example, in talking about primary prevention, we might look for alternatives or substitutive sources of information, to compensate for the inherent loss of hearing.

It is in this early phase that we find there is a critical age beyond which we do not believe that the parts of the subsystem can be altered. It is obvious that we cannot alter the genetic phase. If we are going to affect the proneness or the actual sickness or deviancy or chronicity, we now have to interfere from the environmental side. Such interference from the environmental side is based, of course, on making such environments as are suitable for the particular problem at a particular phase. This involves, naturally, the degree of defect or deficit, which may be deafness alone or deafness with minimal or severe brain damage, or any grade in between.

What Dr. Abdullah has referred to is the fact that the environment still has an effect on systems, even though internally they are not subject to change. Those of us who work with psychologically disturbed patients have a great deal of optimism that although one cannot reorganize the personality and cannot change the personality fundamentally, certain elements in the environment may decrease the degree— or even change the quality—of the deviance, and thus obviate chronicity. Yesterday we were confronted with a miracle, a patient discharged and functioning after many years of hospitalization; and the question was raised in my mind: How can patients who have spent 23 years in a State hospital in a stage of chronicity be reverted back to a stage of acceptable deviance?

Dr. Abdullah has indicated the answer in his scheme. At every phase, in dealing with the existent defect, he believes that the environment that is detrimental to recovery may be changed to ameliorate the process. This, I think, is an extremely fruitful theoretical way of viewing the problems of health and illness, and specifically for those having deafness as well.

Organization of Psychiatric Services
for the Deaf on a Statewide Basis

Dr. John D. Rainer

Dr. Rainer:

At this point I would like to address myself to some of the practical problems involved in setting up mental health services for the deaf.

Yesterday, at the beginning of this workshop, I said there had been a delay in enlisting the personal interest of psychiatrists in this fascinating and vastly important field. But nevertheless we have, here, a tremendous gathering of 30 or 40 psychiatrists who by their very presence show they are now interested in working with the deaf. We have gotten to know you and each other and I think we are now all faced with some of the problems of what to do in our own particular States or localities, to organize these services.

You have undoubtedly gotten by osmosis, if in no other way, over the past 2 days, some idea of the way in which our services are organized. They were organized centrifugally, starting with the need for psychiatric clearance, if you will, of deaf clients of the Division of Vocational Rehabilitation in New York.

The original idea was that some of the clients could not be placed in jobs because of their emotional problems. The feeling was, "Let's find some psychiatrists who can see them and fix them up and send them back to us, and then they can be placed in jobs." This was the core of what was done.

The psychiatrists who were found, Dr. Kallmann and those of us who started with this program, were modest enough to feel that we had to learn a good deal more about the deaf before we could undertake it, and so the whole program centered, first, around deaf adults of vocational age.

From there, further needs developed. We needed to know more about these adult deaf and we undertook to find out more about their adjustment in every sphere of life. We also decided that we needed an outpatient clinic, with sources of referral.

The outpatient clinic was set up. The sources of referral were notified. They included clubs, organizations for the deaf, private practitioners, and deaf people themselves.

When it came to deaf people themselves, we encountered a particular form of resistance in the beginning. This seemed to be peculiar to some of the deaf in New York State, because not everyone I have spoken to has had the same experience. But we began to get some feeling, from some of the deaf organizations and deaf people in New York State, that "We don't want to be singled out. We are not crazy. We don't really need this help. You are asking too many questions," and so on.

We tackled that by holding an affair in this room. I can see it now. It was about 8 years ago. The group of deaf leaders of New York State was about equal in size to the present group. We had them here, and we told them what we were doing. The group included Max Friedman, whom you heard yesterday from the platform. He was one of the leaders in helping us to organize this group.

Next, the deaf representatives went back to their organizations. They passed resolutions, sent out letters, petitioned the legislature and really got behind the plan themselves.

Now we have got to the point where we have, as you know, a Mental Health Association of the Deaf. We also have, in New York State, a recently appointed commission, which is the Temporary New York State Commission to Study Problems of the Deaf, which is made up of prominent deaf laymen, of legislators, and other people who work with the deaf. The purpose of the commission is to investigate the needs, social, psychiatric, and educational, of the deaf residents in the State.

Returning to our program, we proceeded outward and have gone, as you see, back to the school. Starting with a consultant relationship to the school, we have gone into a preventive psychiatric relationship, working with parents, teachers, and cottage staff. As Dr. Altshuler pointed out, we have also gone ahead, to the provision of continuous aftercare, available to the deaf people throughout their periods of need.

But in the first period, the main need that emerged was the need for inpatient service. We felt that we needed to have a ward such as you have seen yesterday, where the patients who need it can be there 24 hours a day under observation and scrutiny, with our being able to get to know them better, and being able to get to them and learn from them. Without such inpatient service, our outpatient service, valuable as it was, lacked something, really, to attach itself to, because as soon as the patient needed to go into a hospital, he had to be admitted to a nearby State hospital. At first we tried to maintain some kind of contact with the hospital, but found that this really wasn't enough.

And so, in 1962, we said that we needed inpatient service, and the establishment of this inpatient service was, from an administrative point of view, not a very easy thing to get established. You see, the outpatient service was part of a research project, financed with Federal funds. It had a limited time and it concluded with a final report in the form of a book.[1] This book represented our findings to date so that other people might go forth with it.

Setting up an inpatient service involved getting the State to agree that, 3 years from the time the service was set up with Federal funds, the State would take it over on a permanent basis.

There was a good deal of discussion at all levels before we could take the initiative. The State said, "We cannot promise what we will be able to do 3 years from now." The Federal Goverment said, "We cannot finance you unless you guarantee you will take it over in 3 years." This went back and forth, and I think that we finally got it as a result of a good deal of talking and convincing through personal contact.

Dr. Kallmann happened to be a long-time personal friend of Paul Hoch, who was Commissioner of Mental Hygiene at the time. Paul Hoch said to Franz Kallmann, "How can you get such an elaborate setup for the deaf when hearing patients in the hospitals don't have all that they need?" The only answer to this argument was, "Well, this is what we're interested in. If we are going to do it, we have to do it in the best way we know how," and so the inpatient service did get established.

Now we have moved over into the aftercare area to establish the need for halfway houses and sheltered workshops. We have a social worker, a rehabilitation counselor, and we are moving to improve our services further.

I don't say that this is the only way to organize such services. Other groups have organized them in other ways. In Europe, for example, in Norway, they have started with the children, which is, I suppose, the more logical way to start. They have started with special psychiatric provision for disturbed deaf children, and this not on a consulting or an ambulatory basis, but through special schools. In Oslo there is a special school, and there is a psychiatrist who devotes half of his time, I believe, to consulting at the school at which these disturbed, multiply handicapped, psychologically handicapped deaf children are not only schooled but treated. From that they hope to move up into the adult area.

---

[1] Rainer, J. D., Altshuler, K. Z., Kallmann, F. J. and Demming, W. E. (eds.). *Family and Mental Health Problems in a Deaf Population*. New York, New York State Psychiatric Institute, 1963.

One of the biggest needs here, I think, is special classes or special schools for these difficult cases. We have the same frustration that we had with our deaf adults who needed inpatient care, who needed hospitalization, before we had our special ward. We experience more or less the same thing with respect to deaf youngsters who cannot remain in the schools, where the schools have no provisions for youngsters who are either extremely withdrawn and psychotic, or extremely disturbed or acting out in one way or another. The need for special schools or special classes for not only the brain damaged but the emotionally disturbed deaf child is a very serious one. It may be that in some other State this would be the place to start.

The provision of proper therapy for various socioeconomic or cultural groups, geared to the degree of early cultural enrichment, is certainly a need which has to be tackled. The support of such programs is not simple to achieve, as those of you in adminstrative positions in various States are undoubtedly well aware.

The degree of support for mental health, in general, varies with the climate of the times, and the support for special programs such as this certainly varies with the degree of interest in mental health in general. There is a general long-range tendency toward provision of special mental health services for special groups—narcotic addicts, alcoholics, the blind. The retarded, of course, have always had special facilities. We know that there is this tendency toward special services for special groups, and it is certainly one which can be extended to include the deaf.

One requisite is that there has to be greater interest among public health agencies. We have been well supported and encouraged by Vocational Rehabilitation Administration, but what about other governmental agencies concerned with mental health? What about mental health associations and social welfare organizations?

Our whole development therefore has been along pragmatic lines. It has come out of the vocational area. But I do think that by this time, and I feel that this assembly shows it, psychiatric work with the deaf is more than just a minor service to which we, as psychiatrists, have to give an hour or two a week. It is becoming not only a subspecialty of great human interest, but an important social need.

I said earlier that I looked forward to the day when there are no more deaf. But I think before that day comes we will have days when there will be more deaf, what with virus infections still playing their part, and so on.

I would like to hear from some of you about suggestions for the development of longitudinal services in your particular areas. There are all these little beginnings, you see. I hope that all of us who have made beginnings will continue to get together. I would hardly venture to suggest forming another psychiatric association, but we might perhaps have meetings such as this without forming an association, to pool our experiences, pool our interests, and perhaps at the American Psychiatric Association meetings we can have gatherings and continue to foster the development of this field.

But something constructive has to be done. The profession, the deaf people themselves, the public at large as well, have to exert pressure upon legislative and fund-giving agencies, because it is obvious that even much less than the hearing, the deaf who need psychiatric services cannot rely on private practice of psychiatrists. Programs have to be set up in some kind of longitudinal manner and for the difficult cases they must include inpatient settings.

We are very glad to again acknowledge the support, for 11 or 12 years, now, of the Vocational Rehabilitation Administration and the consistent help of its consultant, Dr. Boyce Williams. He was unfortunately unable to be here today, but he has been one of the guiding spirits behind this work from its very beginning. We wish also to thank all the other people who have been so cooperative and encouraging.

Dr. Abdullah:

I should like to bring up one other matter. In our work, in New York State, one difficulty is that we have a center for the deaf here in New York City, and patients come from a large area. Can we conceive of any psychiatric services which could reach deaf persons in other areas more easily? We often have to transplant them from neighborhoods where they have grown up, a great distance away from their families.

Dr. Rainer:

This is a problem that came up in the northwest part of England. There has been a lot of interest in setting up a special hospital ward for the deaf in mental hospitals. Dr. R. W. Eldridge, health officer, and Dr. John Denmark, who is the son of the superintendent of a school for the deaf, have been interested in setting up something of the sort, but they have had to answer arguments from those who feel that the decentralization of mental health facilities takes precedence over bringing the deaf together into one hospital and that patients should be nearer to their home surroundings. Ideally, this plan would probably be a good one. In New York State, where we have a large population, it has always been on our minds. We still have a plan, which is somewhere on the shelf for the time being, but it just isn't feasible at this point to establish another center upstate, near Syracuse or Rochester.

In smaller States, however, there may not be enough deaf people in the whole State to warrant such an elaborate setting. It may be necessary to have regional settings of some kind covering a number of States.

Dr. Sonnega:

To what extent have leaders in deaf education, around the country, been able to communicate their feelings about this language-lipreading training controversy, and are there problems to be anticipated in liaison between mental health services who take a different view? Has there been any rapprochement between these groups?

Dr. Rainer:

We have tried to steer a middle course, and as long as we were working with adults we could do so pretty easily, because we said we had to take the patients as they come and communicate with them as they communicate. When you get down to the younger and younger age group, of course, you get closer and closer to the controversy.

The educators of the deaf, in the beginning, also had some of the mistrust that the deaf community had. For a long time—for a century, perhaps—the educators of the deaf had been the ones who were giving the psychiatric treatment, who were doing the psychiatric diagnosis, taking care of the mental health problems of their pupils as well as they could. They probably didn't have too much success, actually, in enlisting the help of psychiatrists; so that maybe they had a point, that psychiatrists weren't going to be of much help anyhow. But gradually, at least in our State, they have asked for and accepted our help in school problems.

Dr. Altshuler:

There are two studies currently underway with regard to young students, as they are being taught by the oral method alone, and as they are being taught by mixed methods. It will be of great interest to see the results.

It seems to me when we speak to educators, that the very beginning of a swingback in the other direction, away from the purity of oralism, is to be noted. These two studies, if they go the way their preliminary reports indicate, should do a lot to confirm and add a little impetus to that swing. It is not an answer to the present situation, but it may be in the future.

Dr. Schlesinger:

Although the parents in the Bay area know that I sign, those who are quite vocal about their endorsement of the oral method have invited me to be a speaker and have also referred their children as patients.

I think that a rapprochement with the parents and the educators, even though they are quite clearly on one side of the controversy, can be achieved at the administrative and clinical level.

Dr. Rainer:

Yes, I believe we have to go back still further, even before the school, to the interaction between the parents and children. In this connection, the Deaf Baby Program that we heard about yesterday is important. I suppose for completeness I should mention also homes for the aged. We have, somehow, to make this a complete cradle-to-the-grave program. I think there is no other way.

Experiences and Programs of the Conference Participants

Alternative Communication Systems for the Deaf

Dr. Peter F. Ostwald

Dr. Ostwald:

A great many of the theoretical points that have been brought up in this last discussion rest on the development of an adequate understanding of the very early symbolic systems used for communication. Information of this type, unfortunately, is badly lacking in normal personality development, and it really seems too early to begin to make comparisons between, for example, the ego development of the deafened child and the development of the normal child.

There are some ways, nevertheless, that we can begin to use to approach the problem. I will first mention the importance of being able to detect so-called deafness early enough. We are very limited, at the present time, in terms of when we can say with any degree of certainty that a youngster is deaf. What we are in the process of doing is developing ways of perhaps coming a little closer to this notion of what is a deaf child and what is a hearing child during the first year of life.

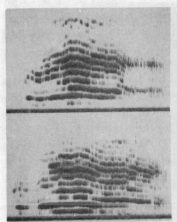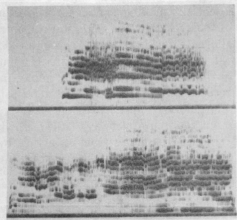

FIGURE 4.

A method I am particularly interested in has to do with the acoustic spectrographic study of the infant's cry. Figure 4 illustrates how this can be done. Here is some material from an earlier study of infant twins,[1] showing cries of one pair of identical twins on the left, and of a pair of fraternal twins on the right.

This method, which we are beginning to call cry printing, has a kind of simple way of describing converted sound, which essentially is an early affect expression of the baby converted into a visual structure which can be scanned and analyzed in terms of a number of acoustical properties that I won't go into at this moment. It seems to me that this would be a very fruitful way to approach the whole question of the Anlage, the early determinants for affective communication as between the infant and his mother.

We are starting to use the cry prints, also, to look at the cooing and the onset of babbling. It might just be possible that we can begin to make some statement about disturbances of communication during the first year of life by studying this type of material.

Dr. Callaway, our neurophysiologist, is also exploring the possibility of applying the average of evoked potential studies as a way of determining whether the brain is actually able to receive and incorporate into its structure the information provided by auditory input.

The next point is the great importance of replacing in some way the kind of information that is lost to the deaf child. We have been talking, actually, about what happens to people when they do not have auditory input. Dr. Altshuler mentioned the loss of emotive cues, and the loss of language cues, and something about the loss of distance cues.

It is quite likely that there are certain critical periods at which the youngster must be stimulated with this kind of information if he is going to develop an ego capable of dealing with the world. What I am essentially making a pitch for is greater exploration and development of tools whereby the youngster can obtain this kind of information by alternate routes, primarily through vision.

I titled this report Alternative Communications Systems, and I want to thank Dr. Schlesinger for giving me the idea of the alternatives, because I think it is a mistake to talk about substitutions. It has a certain pejorative quality. What we're trying to do is to provide more input and to use every available method for doing this.

Figure 5 is taken from an article by D. B. Fry,[2] to illustrate the different possibilities for providing alternative inputs.

---

[1] Ostwald, P. F., Freedman, D. G. and Kurtz, J. H. Vocalization of infant twins. *Folia Phoniat.*, *14:* 37–50, 1962.

[2] Fry, D. B. The experimental study of speech. In *Studies in Communication*. London, Martin Secker & Warburg, 1955. Pp. 143–167.

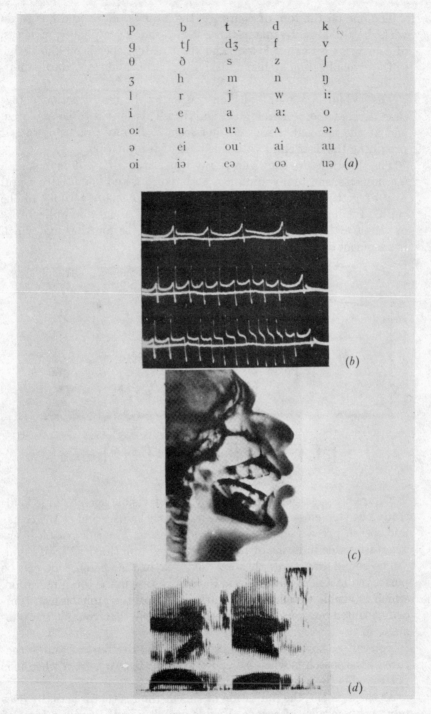

FIGURE 5.

The one on the top, of course, is the most familiar, and has to do with the alphabet. In this instance it is a phonetic alphabet, which is, of course, a very valuable tool, and yet it really depends on knowledge of the symbolization system underlying written and printed communication.

The second is a simple demonstration of the use of action potentials derived from neurological activity. This is still to be explored, and at the moment there does not seem to be any practical way of providing the deaf child with this kind of information.

The third picture shows an X-ray illustration of the human speech mechanisms, and to my mind it is an important and potentially useful way of getting information about speech and motor activity to the child. (I will get back to this shortly when I talk about the applicability of visible articulation.) Now I want to turn to the fourth thing, which is a segment of visible speech.

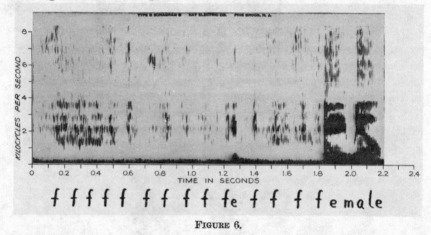

FIGURE 6.

Figure 6 is a larger, blown-up picture of visible speech. This is already one step closer to the actual motor mechanism and to the dynamic speech process underlying communication. For this reason it has a certain value in terms of potentially providing the deaf with input.

The sound structures that are involved in the speech code can be portrayed in a more naturalistic way, as you see in the top illustration, which is visible speech. Underneath it you see the alphabetical, typically printed-out version of speech, and under that you get the phonetics of it.

You can see how different the actual flow and rhythm and sonic structure of the speech is when it is portrayed in this way, from when it is portrayed in the usual alphabetical sequences.

At the moment, the limitation of this method is that it actually does rely on knowledge of a code. Visible speech is still largely a kind of code which has to be learned, and the learning of this is pretty laborious, even for the normal individual. I think it is too much of a task for the deaf person to learn it, even though there have been some experiments and some positive results with it. But newer items are being developed, and the Bell Telephone Company has now got something which can be called a device to produce visible articulations.

I mentioned the sound X-ray motion picture in which you can see the speech processes in action. Obviously, you cannot do this for long periods of time because of the danger of overexposure to X-ray radiation, but for short intervals you can provide the deaf person with a direct feedback of his own articulation, which he can then immediately correct or modulate, in terms of the normal picture, a movie of the more normal speech articulation.

What the newer methods can do is to convert the information from the sound output directly into a visual analogue, which is portrayed on a screen. The deaf person can then see the movements of his lips, his tongue, his throat in action as he is speaking, and through direct visual feedback he can begin to make corrections and can produce something which would come closer and closer to the normal speech movements and thereby naturally also the normal speech sounds.

I think this is a very important development, and something that I hope you will all bear in mind in connection with work that you may be doing with the deaf.

It is a relatively simple device. It consists of a long tube. As the technology improves, I am sure it will be shortened. The deaf person simply speaks into it, and by way of two little microphones the impedance changes in that tube are measured and come out converted by computer into speech display.

There are a number of other gadgets and devices that are very useful and important in this connection. I personally think it is essential that we get hold of picturephones, because of the necessity for visual imputs and for the deaf person to be able to see the individual who is at the other end of the telephone circuit and be able to use signs over the telephone lines.

I am very much in favor of this kind of development, and of every possible utilization of teletypewriters, of voice-activated typewriters, and of handwriting communications over long distances, and finally, of the picturephone.

There are many problems involved since the whole problem of language translation by way of computer is a very difficult one, and in many ways, at the present time, an unsolved one.

However, I think there is every reason to be extremely optimistic that modern technology, which has been so successful in terms of satellites and outer space communication, can also help us a great deal in our investigations of the problems of the deaf, and also in connection with the treatment of the deaf.

Cultural and Environmental Influences in the Emotional Development of the Deaf

Dr. Hilde Schlesinger

Dr. Schlesinger:

I would like to focus on some of the aspects of early environment and later interpersonal relationships which might contribute to the cognitive and emotional development of deaf youngsters and adults.

These influences have been frequently mentioned during these last 2 days. I have had some indication that some of the findings referred to, both by Dr. Levine [3] previously and by the group at New York, compare quite closely to findings in environmentally handicapped youngsters, youngsters that the Office of Economic Opportunity is interested in, who show very similar profiles.

This led us to speculate that the difficulty may be due not to deafness but to environmentally produced deprivation of those cultural factors shared by the middle-class American culture. In order to clarify some of this, I would like to state how I conceptualize the deaf child.

Let us imagine an American child with relatively conflict-free parents. These parents will feel relatively secure with their cultural standards, and will have relatively little difficulty communicating the idea to their children that this is a good way to live. This is, unquestionably, a good way to acquire a healthy ethnocentered self esteem.

Carried to a slightly higher degree, the parents say, "As for those with different cultures or languages, they would surely emulate us, if they could." Carried to what I consider unhealthy extremes, this ethnocentrism then becomes, "You must emulate us."

---

[3] Levine, E. S. *Youth in a Soundless World.* New York, New York University Press, 1956.

Let us bear in mind that children of all cultures will feel similarly that my way—whether it is French, Italian, or German—is pretty good, at that.

Studies of immigrant children indicates that those with the healthiest ethnocentric outlook, those who least feel the need to deny their place of origin or their background, adjust most easily to America, and learn English more quickly. There is evidence to show that bilingualism in children does not hinder either language. So long as both languages are acceptable within the overall culture and the parents speak in both languages, there will be relatively little conflict in the use of the two languages.

There is also psychoanalytical evidence of the dynamic use of language in psychotherapy as regards choice of language, intonation, or the increase or decrease of accent.

It is clear that conceptually, deaf youngsters living within two cultures—the larger hearing America and the smaller deaf culture—have a language of their own. How likely is it that a deaf child will acquire this healthy ethnocentrism which appears to contribute to emotional and cognitive growth? Even assuming relatively conflict-free parents, it must be quite difficult.

There is some indication that deaf children do better in this respect when they have deaf parents. A sociologist at the University of California, Dr. K. Meadow, has kindly permitted me to share with you some of her recent and unpublished findings, comparing two groups of youngsters at the California school who were matched on the WISC Intelligence Test. Deaf children of deaf parents were studied by several means, and found to differ significantly in the Stanford Achievement Test, in positive self esteem, and in communicative abilities of most types.

The deaf child, usually already handicapped by the loss of one of the senses which can accurately portray the world about him, might not easily get the environmental enrichment he requires in childhood. It has been well demonstrated by a number of investigators that an individual needs some type of gratifying communication; otherwise disturbance will result. The infant needs to go through varied but definite and progressive experiences of maturation in the perception of the mother, for example, in order to acquire appropriate knowledge of himself and the world.

There is evidence that some deaf youngsters have some type of interference with the normative, perceptual-motor sequence, an interference which may occur either through organic defects, maturational disorders, or some vicissitudes of pyschological development, such as precocious expectations or urban behavior demands. This abnormality in perceptual-motor sequence appears to be of some importance in the development of emotional disturbances in physically intact youngsters, as well as bringing about many of the features of emotional disturbance in sensory-deprived, blind or deaf youngsters. These children will often engage in special perceptual-motor maneuvers in an attempt to replace or make up for the deficit in the developmental sequence. Many of these maneuvers have playful, socially acceptable features, while others become annoying stereotyped gestures or repetitive motions. Still others fit the classic pathological symptoms.

Some authors believe that the stereotyped autistic gestures of the schizophrenic fit into this category of perceptual-motor disorders, while many educators talk of blindisms and deafisms as correlating quite highly with symptoms of autistic youngsters. In any case, one must be carefully aware of the above developmental possibilities in determining the extent of some cognitive difficulties as well as emotional disturbances.

Among the young deaf, the mother-child relationship becomes doubly important. The way in which the mother is able to respond to the child's emotion, which might be expressed through its reflexes or by more sophisticated expressions of a need, depends in a large part on her own self-esteem and ego integrity. Some disturbed mothers have interpreted a child's reflex action as indicating rejection or disobedience. Similarly, Dorothy Burlingham [4] has shown many mothers of blind infants are distressed by the particular way the blind child expresses attentiveness, with a quiet attitude which makes the child appear almost withdrawn, but which makes for better hearing.

In this study, mothers very frequently were found to misinterpret this attitude to mean that the child does not pay attention, for attentiveness in the blind is not as we normally expect it; i.e., with vision limited toward the stimulus and the body straining toward it. This has frequently resulted in overstimulation by these parents with a subsequent anxiety on the part of both children and parents, and often producing solitary, autoerotic activity, misconstrued as being an accompaniment of blindness.

Similar features are seen in deafness. The usual avenues of communication are different and the usual mutual relaxation between mother and child is frequently disturbed. The parents desperately want the child to be like themselves, and frequently they achieve the exact opposite of their desires. I have seen some anxious parents of deaf children so desirous of teaching normalcy to their offspring that

---

[4] Burlingham, D. Hearing and its role in the development of the blind. *Psych. Study of Child, 19:* 95–112, 1964.

they refuse to sign and sat on their hands while communicating with their youngsters.

When a deaf child grows up, he is aware that others about him playfully and easily learn how to communicate verbally, while to him this is a laborious undertaking. Furthermore, he must know that there is for him an easier system of communication, which is not entirely accepted by the society around him. It is forbidden, or surreptitiously used, or blatantly ignored; and when it is ignored or forbidden, the birth of esoteric language can often be observed.

Even when the manual form of communication is surreptitiously used, the children still learn that one of their native tongues is not quite as good, not quite as acceptable, as the spoken language—a concept which may certainly interfere with the development of the healthy ethnocentrism referred to above.

It would even appear that many deaf youngsters behave with a massive negativism toward the spoken language because of the frequency and intensity with which they may receive the message, "You are good only if you behave and communicate the way I wish you to." When in contact with individuals who are fully accepting of them, with or without speech, the negativism may no longer be necessary, and the learning of both language and speech may proceed with greater ease.

Group Psychotherapy With Hospitalized Deaf Patients

Dr. Luther Robinson

Dr. Robinson:

As an employee of the Federal Government, I must begin with a bureaucratic disclaimer to the effect that any opinion which I express here is my own and not that of the Federal Government or HEW or St. Elizabeths Hospital. This also applies to what I shall be saying about our psychiatric program for the deaf.

My program's mission at St. Elizabeth is not primarily working with the deaf. I came to this out of my own interest in language, and after taking a course in sign language and finger spelling on my own time back in 1963, I decided that perhaps I could put to some use what I had learned.

I combed the wards of St. Elizabeths and came up with six or seven deaf patients who were able to communicate by sign language and finger spelling. I thought that six would make a good group, and so I started group psychotherapy, or at least what I called group psychotherapy, because I had never heard of group psychotherapy with deaf patients before.

I felt like the little child trying to draw a picture of God. When her mother told her that no one had ever seen God and that no one knew what God looked like, she said, "Well, when I get through, they will know."

I am not at all sure that you will know what my kind of group psychotherapy is, or if you will call it that after I have given my description. The group consisted of six members, four men and two women. Their ages ranged from 29 to 70, with a mean age of 43.5. They had spent some time of their early lives in schools for the deaf, but all had speech and hearing handicaps ranging from severe to profound.

Their intellectual levels also varied widely. Their periods of hospitalization ranged from 8 to 21 years, with a mean period of 16 years, and among the six patients the diagnoses included four schizophrenic reactions, one psychotic disorder without clearly defined structural change in the brain, and one chronic brain syndrome of unknown or unspecified cause, with behavioral reactions.

During the course of their hospitalization, these patients had individually shown such symptoms as catatonic stupor, posturing, mannerisms, urinary incontinence, gesticulating, pacing, alternation in appetite, acting out, delusions, and hallucinations, with some remissions and exacerbations, of course. As a subgroup in the hospital, their common characteristics included social isolation, inferiority feelings, and problems in interpersonal relationships.

What did I do as a therapist with such a group as this? All I could do was to use what I had learned from working with hearing patients. This was a matter of attempting to establish rapport with the patients in a group setting, observing and evaluating dynamics, and assisting the patients in modifying their behavior toward more healthy ways of interacting.

In a group such as this, where there are wide differences in communication skills and in intellectual levels, the therapist has got to be very active. He permits the use of whatever communication skills are available. But for this particular group we used sign language and finger spelling as the primary mode of communication.

Since sign language has a more concrete quality than verbal language, it does not permit an exact, word-for-word substitute for verbal language; and moreover, there are colloquial variations in signs and meanings. Therefore, we had to spend a considerable amount of time clarifying content.

Now, about the place we selected for therapy: The therapy room had to be well illuminated and it had to have a minimum of visual distractions because of the marked dependence of communication on visual concentration. The seating arrangement was circular or semi-circular, to afford maximum visual contact among the members.

Because of the exploratory nature of the procedure, I used a variety of techniques, including nondirective, directive, and supportive. Sometimes the discussion evoked marked anxiety, and this was dealt with by trying to draw various members into the conversation. Occasionally, the group members expressed hostile feelings about their hearing handicaps, about hospitalization, relatives, doctors, other authority figures, and even about other patients.

But during the early sessions I already observed some striking similarities of this group to hearing groups. I noticed that group members soon established certain distinctive roles. Thus, one was a leader, and another an obstructionist, and still another a mediator; one was a sleeper and still another a teaser. And these roles they maintained throughout the sessions. Other similarities to hearing groups included the formation of subgroups within the group, to the exclusion of some members and sometimes even to the exclusion of the therapist.

On the other hand, I noticed as well some differences from hearing groups, and these differences were most striking in the area of affective responses. I think that this matter of the affective qualities has been mentioned earlier. The responses I noticed were unrestrained laughter, sympathy, hostility, touching, and other expressions of feeling tone. After about a year and a half of this, I thought that perhaps I had better list all of these responses. I tried to recall every single response that I had observed over the year and a half, and I came up with about 18. I divided these into nonconversational and conversational. Among some of the nonconversational I included attentiveness, smiling, touching, laughing, sleeping, teasing, hostility, anger. As for the conversational responses, I further divided these into manual communication only, manual communication with intelligible vocalization, manual communication with unintelligible vocalization, intelligible vocalization only, and unintelligible vocalization only.

We wanted to observe all of these responses, and so I arranged for a hearing observer, a social worker, who had been trained in sign language, in finger spelling, as well as in group work. I had this observer sit in the group, and after a period of indoctrination we tried to develop a crude rating system, a scale, for these responses. We wanted to check these out from four different aspects: Intragroup nonconversational responses, intragroup conversational responses, the interaction among patients, and the response to the therapist.

When I refer to intragroup responses I don't mean what went on between one patient and another, but what went on as a general group response.

In the interaction responses, I wanted to know what went on between one patient and another, and I also wanted to know whether the patients responded to one other patient only, or to two or more.

The fourth aspect was the response to the therapist. How did the patient respond to the therapist?

The hearing observer sat in for 12 weeks. After each session we scored these various responses. Then for 12 more weeks I wanted to go further. I wanted to know if it is possible that a deaf observer would score these responses the same way as the hearing observer would. But we had no trained deaf observer, and so, to compromise, we had the services of a student from Gallaudet College who is majoring in psychology and sociology and who wanted to get some experience in group work. We had him sit in the group for 12 additional sessions, together with the hearing observer. After each session we asked the hearing observer to score the responses as if through the eyes of the deaf person. We did not expect to get anything scientifically valid out of this, but it was an interesting operation, nonetheless.

We did this for 12 more sessions, so that we had a total of 12 with the hearing observer and then 12 with the hearing and the deaf observer. This is what we found:

For intragroup responses, exclusive of conversation, over a 6-month period, the two 12-week sessions were similar as judged by the scoring of the hearing observer. For intragroup responses, exclusive of conversation, over the 6-month period, attentiveness, smiling and mannerisms, using the face, ranked highest. Mannerisms, using the body, and hallucinations were low, while delusions were absent.

For intragroup responses, average scale score of responses for the 6-month period was highest for manual communication; that is, for the intragroup conversation.

For interaction responses among patients, the patients seemed to respond more to two observers than to one alone. The responses were of the same order of magnitude, from one patient to other patients, as they were between the patients and the therapist.

Much of the data we collected needs further analysis, and we will not at this time attempt to draw any conclusions. I feel that I have to report to you, though, that the patient who responded the least, who slept the most, and who smiled the most, is the only one whom we have been able to place in a situation of gainful employment out in the community.

Such a rating scale could be of value if we could refine our techniques and develop a rating scale of responses in group psychotherapy with the deaf. Perhaps such a scale could have some predictive value for therapeutic response, or perhaps we could correlate these responses in group therapy with an accompanying social and vocational adjustment scale.

This would suggest the value of a social worker or a vocational rehabilitation counselor as an observer in the group.

Beyond this, this kind of rating scale might be used to assist in training deaf people in doing group work with patients. Such a scale could also be used to compare the way deaf people evaluate behavior as compared to the way hearing people evaluate the same behavior.

I have always felt that group psychotherapy was of little value if it was done in isolation, and therefore it was necessary to develop other aspects of a psychiatric program for the deaf.

Since we started, our deaf patients have doubled in number and our program has just about tripled in size. We now have a multidisciplinary program, and I have been able to get the help of many of the other workers at the hospital who have hearing patients as their primary concern. I have been able to get them to study sign language and finger spelling, and to devote about an hour a week to our deaf program. Moreover, we have been able to get hearing patients to take a course in sign language and finger spelling, in order to communicate with deaf patients better in the wards where our deaf patients are scattered.

Diagnostic Evaluation of Hearing-Impaired Children

Dr. James A. Sonnega

Dr. Sonnega:

How did the teaching to the deaf of oral language without sign language persist for such a long period? My own experience has been totally in an area and setting where only oral language is taught, and is colored by that fact. Our approach to treatment is of necessity concentrated on communication only to the extent that a formal language system was developed, aside from the usual methods we use with children in adolescence to help them to relate.

Our general approach to evaluation of hard-of-hearing and deaf children—and I will mention in just a moment why we chose not to make such a distinction—has been in terms of a scalar evaluation, employing the usual methods of history, reports from other workers, and direct observation by an interdisciplinary team.

Aside from the pressing clinical need of finding a solution in terms of available resources, we have also been much intrigued by the relationship between language, thought, and personality. We have decided to use a functional approach in evaluating our patients' auditory system, and have not been able, frequently, to decide whether a child should be called deaf or hard-of-hearing. Throughout our work we have tried to avoid labels which might prejudice anyone against working with the child.

We have concentrated not only on auditory sensitivity tests, but also on tests of auditory perception, including at times the use of filters and also more sophisticated audiometric studies, such as oral overload, in an effort to define just what the auditory problem is. It is quite easy to distinguish between conductive and nerve-type impairment, but when one gets into evaluating the effects of the audiometric contour on auditory perception, it becomes a more fuzzy matter since it appears that perception of speech signals, at least, can be impaired on the basis of the audiometric contour, but also on the basis of the cochlear dysfunction, and at times dysfunction in the auditory nerve and beyond.

So we work very closely with audiologists in an attempt to evaluate what the auditory capabilities of the child actually are. This is also very necessary when we attempt to evaluate his language system.

Muriel Morley has shown the relationship between audiometric patterns and the growth of various linguistic variables,[5] and the Ewings in England have been interested in the relationship between the growth of language and the growth of primarily mental intellectual processes along the lines of Piaget.[6]

When we tried to evaluate intelligence we ran into problems for several reasons. I was much interested in some of the comments con-

[5] Morley, M. E. *The Development and Disorders of Speech in Childhood* (2d ed.). Baltimore, Williams and Wilkins, 1965.

[6] Ewing, A. W. G. *Linguistic Development and Mental Growth in Hearing Impaired Children* Volta Review 65:180–187, 1963.

cerning the personalities of the adult and adolescent deaf patients. We found that although we could gain a measure of a child's intellectual capability and performance items, we could not have the same comfort of generalizing from these functions to the capacity of the child to learn language.

For instance, we have had several deaf patients with atrophy of the left hemisphere in whom the performance scores on the Wechsler Intelligence Scale for children were completely within normal limits.

We found that it is a much fuzzier issue when one attempts to generalize from performance or spatial perceptual functions to the capacity for symbolic thinking. In the group of children whom we have been evaluating over the last few years, we found a much higher incidence of brain damage than reported in the literature; at least for the classrooms for hard-of-hearing and deaf children in Oakland County, which comprise about 250 children. Well over half of the children have tainted birth and developmental histories, and show other signs, soft signs, of organicity. They have many of the findings commonly seen in brain-damaged children.

Incidentally, we also found an increased incidence of left handedness, which has interested us and puzzled us. I see that this is also found in your adult deaf group. There are a number of groups, as you know, where left handedness is twice the normal incidence. This suggests, perhaps, that there is some relationship between the asymmetric localization of the function in the brain having to do with language systems, and the development of handedness. I am certain that the genetics involved are very complex, and are, in all probability, multifactorial.

When we do a scalar diagnosis, we are interested in such variables as neurological integration, motility patterns, functioning IQ as measured by clinic psychologists, intellectual capacity as inferred from the audiometric pattern, our own clinical assessment, the psychologist's impression, the teacher's impression. We make a group enterprise out of this attempt to get some idea of what the intellectual capacity might be.

In addition, we evaluate the child's relationship, capacity and formation, his anxiety, both exogenous and endogenous, and self esteem, along with his ego boundaries. Those of you interested in this scale will find it has been reported by Charles Shaw in his recent book *Psychiatric Disorders of Children.*[7]

What has come out of our study has been the general belief that the same factors that underlie the development of meaningful inter-

---

[7] Shaw, C. *The Psychiatric Disorders of Children,* New York, Appleton-Century-Crofts, 1966.

personal relations, the kind of discriminations and generalizations and associations made, in large part underlie the development of meaningful language.

It is well documented that children subject to experiential deprivation often suffer in terms of language development. It appears that their capacity becomes constricted and possibly so impaired that the damage becomes irreparable. Whether this is true or not in terms of the deaf probably is a moot point.

We have special questions in extending psychiatric services to the deaf child, which have to do with some of the clinical problems that we have presented to us. The majority of deaf and hard-of-hearing children who come to Hawthorne Center for evaluation come for the same reasons that their hearing counterparts do, namely, academic underachievement, some question of language and reading retardation beyond their level, which might be predicted from the teacher's impression and from test scores, and impulsive aggressive acting out.

Uniformly, the acting out of the deaf children that we have seen has been of the unpremeditated impulsive variety. We have wondered, too, whether the kinds of psychological defenses available to the deaf are to some degree related to the lack of symbolic skills and the use of verbal mediation in social problem solution.

In the preschool period, where differential diagnosis is hazardous— to say the least—we have been unable to make a concomitant diagnosis of schizophrenia and congenital deafness. In fact, we have searched for 5 years, and we have not found anyone who has been willing to make such a diagnosis.

We have found, however, in some of the young schizophrenic children whom we have called "language impaired", that as something happens in terms of maturation, as their language systems mature, their delusion formation becomes more apparent. But strictly on behavioral grounds, we have been unable to make a diagnosis of schizophrenia in congenitally deafened children.

Our problem, which I would like to pose to you, has to do with the planning for mental health facilities for deaf youngsters: Whether it would be advisable to attach to a school for the deaf, or to a county, or to a school system, a psychiatric and psychological and social work facility, or whether this kind of work should be carried out in a residential treatment center. The problem with children and adolescents has to do with providing them with adequate education, in terms of costs and availability of personnel. At this point, at least in Michigan, we are uncertain as to which way to go. If any of you have had any experience in this matter, I would certainly appreciate hearing about it.

A Pilot Program for the Deaf in a State Hospital
Dr. Miguel Gracia

Dr. Gracia:

My work as staff psychiatrist at Warm Springs (Montana) State Hospital began in January 1961, in a male chronic service called the Continued Treatment Male Service. It included a fluctuating population of about 300 patients, with many different diagnostic categories, mainly chronic schizophrenics, chronic brain syndromes of different types, some with mental deficiency and also epileptic conditions. There were a few suffering with manic-depressive reactions.

In general the more active male chronic and subchronic patients were in this area of the hospital, with a range in ages from the early teens to some geriatric cases, or younger ones with presenile or senile conditions. These patients were from open or semiopen or closed wards. Behavior difficulties were part of the main problems, with some younger patients demonstrating antisocial and sociopathic tendencies. This last group particularly required a great amount of the staff attention because of the necessity of organization and discipline.

Among these patients we had a small group suffering with deafness, before being admitted to the hospital, besides other mental symptoms, such as schizophrenic conditions, mental deficiency, or behavior reactions. In all we had six deaf patients, already well accepted by most of the rest of the patients. The one newer patient had a schizophrenic reaction typified by delusional thinking, great distortion of reality, religious confusion and paranoid ideation. He was a single man, in his late 30's, living with his mother not far from the hospital; until the moment of admission to the hospital he had been able to support himself working on farms and ranches. This patient was placed on tranquilizers and individual psychotherapy, and was seen once a week for about 2 months, and then at less regular intervals. His mother remained interested in the patient and eventually, after several months in the hospital, he was released to her care.

This patient was later readmitted to the hospital, after over 2 years outside, and again after a short stay he was discharged and is again self-supporting. This particular patient will communicate with the therapist through pantomime and guttural sounds, hand signs and written statements, this last method being most effective.

At this point we already had recognized an interest in, and attempt at, communication on the part of other patients not suffering with deafness or mutism with those in that category; in fact, about four or five patients were involved in this spontaneous program of communication. The therapist interviewed them individually and explored their interest in the subject. All of them indicated their interest, and were advised and encouraged to continue with it. They were also asked to help the therapist to communicate with the deaf patients through sign language, which some of the patients were in some way mastering through personal interest and practice. One observation by the therapist at this time was a gain in satisfaction and confidence by those patients who were helping the therapist to reach the deaf patients, and acquiring a sense of importance because they were helping the doctor and the staff. Their behavior, too, started to improve. This was at the end of 1961 and early in 1962. At the end of 1962 it was decided to organize some group therapy in this area of the hospital, where group therapy has been done sporadically in previous years in small groups.

Group therapy sessions were organized for two to three groups a week, 1 hour weekly, in groups of 10 to 12 patients, all males, of different ages and diagnostic categories. In selecting the patients for the groups, consultation was done with the registered nurse in the service, attendants, supervisors, psychologists, industrial therapists, as well as recreation personnel, attendants, and social workers, during a number of meetings, mainly service conferences. Patients were selected following different criteria mainly on therapeutic needs and on motivation. Remotivation therapy was in progress in the Continued Treatment services of the hospital, male and female, involving several nurses, nurses aides, and attendants, involving around 200 patients. Deafness was not considered as a handicap. The deaf patients were selected as other patients were. We found later that as a maximum we had three deaf patients in one group, one deaf patient in one group as a minimum, and that some groups had none.

We used one student nurse as recorder in each group. She sat to the left of the leader or therapist, both sitting at the extreme of a long rectangular table, with patients sitting around the table, and in other chairs to the right of the therapist. The door of the room had the proper sign for no interruptions. Patients were free to select their seats. As usually happens, they followed a pattern during successive sessions. The deaf patients always tried to be close to the therapist and the recorder. Their attitude was always very attentive, friendly, smiling often, and communicating at times with hand signs, or written statements, usually at the end of the sessions.

Only one patient suffering with a chronic schizophrenic reaction, paranoid type, would take his seat in one of the groups, to the left of the therapist, and far away at the table. Often he would have his eyes closed, using a lot of nonverbal communication to express his negativistic feelings and hostility to the group. This patient could talk with some speech impediment, and he had some amount of deafness. The group in general handled him well; in a way they isolated him at first. Later he was accepted into the group. This patient at the end of one period of group therapy, which usually lasted from 2½ to 3 months, showed one of his best improvements.

In the sessions we had no limitations of subjects of discussions. The therapist played a flexible role, at times using little or no verbalization, at times more active with regular verbal participation, encouraging the group to participate, using both indirect or direct approaches. Sometimes there was a great amount of generalization of subjects. Patients in general spoke about going home, complaining about the food, outside privileges, freedom, the hospital in general, sex, religion, their families, jobs, medication, electric shock treatment, etc.; about the present, the past, and some about the future. The deaf patients followed the verbalization very well, mainly with visual contacts, and expressed their approval through smiling and nodding. Family matters, the past, advice about behavior, were accepted by the deaf patients very well.

Groups were open to new members if some of the patients for one reason or another had to be replaced, because of physical illness, transfer to another ward due to behavior difficulties, and so on. Frequently the groups would remain functioning with three or four patients missing, and this was handled very well by the patients. To the deaf patients these changes in the group did not matter at all, and at times it seemed that they enjoyed the smaller groups, perhaps because they received more personal attention.

We never found difficulties with the deaf patients not being accepted by the group, and this was already the case in the wards. They were good patients in the sessions, with a great amount of nonverbal participation, and were friendly. Their behavior improved; they seemed happier in the wards and easier to handle. Their personal appearance was better at the end of each period of group therapy. These patients were under the general therapeutic program of the hospital, including the taking of tranquilizers or antidepressants, general chemotherapy, activities therapy, recreation, and so on.

In summary we found that group therapy:

(1) Contributed to reinforce and establish better communication between the deaf patients and the rest of the patients not suffering with this handicap,

(2) Proved a good therapeutic tool in dealing with deaf patients,

(3) Created interest in the deaf among other patients who were not deaf, and a willingness to help them.

In those patients engaged in therapeutic individual sessions, we noticed an increased sense of usefulness, and some amount of pride. Of these patients, more than half left the hospital, through vocational rehabilitation programs, discharge, or convalescence leave.

Of the deaf patients, as already mentioned, one is out of the hospital, employed and self-supporting as a laborer. The others are still in the hospital, but they seem happier. Lack of interest on the part of their relatives, or lack of outside resources, created limitations in dealing with the rehabilitation of these cases. On the other hand we believe that a more intense, better-organized program for learning sign language, under proper leadership and perhaps with some mechanical or electronic devices (for which financial expenditures would be required), could help improve the opportunities of these patients who seem to react well to therapy in a psychiatric environment.

This program, where group therapy is basic, is still going on. We plan to continue with it and make some improvements, following advice and suggestions that we always welcome.

In summary, we can say that this was a very small group of deaf male patients involved in a therapeutic situation, mixed in with a large population of chronic male patients in a State hospital community; the patients involved in even this small-scale program showed indications of therapeutic improvement in a period of over 4 years. With better techniques and ideas, even more improvement is expected.

Discussion

Dr. Altshuler:

I should like to emphasize one point which was made yesterday, that I think we may not have made strongly enough today. That is the aftercare of the deaf inpatient. Our experience indicates that it requires a great deal more active participation on the part of staff than does the aftercare of most other hospital patients. It requires close followup and close liaison with employers. It is an absolute necessity for the post-hospital patients in this group.

Dr. Abdullah:

One important aspect of the group development in our case is that the group has been an ongoing process in our ward. As such, it has gradually developed its own traditions and its own norms. As patients get discharged and new ones come, we have actually witnessed an increase in the level of discussion. This is clearly shown in our book [8] where we have given two protocols, one from the very early group and one from the recent one. In the beginning, we used to sit back and let the patients do most of the talking. We found that discussions would tend to come down to the level of discussing the quality of the food or the potatoes and the faucets and the curtains. Nothing seemed to be going on.

Then we became more active as therapists, and tried to increase the level of discussion; for example, to discuss mothers. We used to have topics in the back of our minds, and somehow we managed to get them discussed. Then, gradually we again got into the role where we don't have to do that. The group has become more sophisticated in their level of discussion. Their level of understanding has increased, and it has become sort of a schooling process, where when the new patient comes in, he is not told anything directly, but he picks up the level himself. It has become a sort of campus atmosphere, where the tradition is continuous.

Dr. Brummit:

I am connected with a school for the deaf in New York City. We have about 600 pupils, about 70 to 80 percent of whom are poor, Negro and Puerto Rican children.

The New York public school system, like that of most large cities, has a great number of indigent pupils who are not academically oriented, as were the middle class schools, which many of us here may have attended. As a result these children underachieve in school. The teachers too often have little ability to communicate with them, do not understand the culture very well, and in addition deny the fact that they do not understand the culture or how to communicate or to teach.

---

[8] Rainer, J. D. and Altshuler, K. Z. *Comprehensive Mental Health Services for the Deaf.* New York, New York State Psychiatric Institute, 1966.

Inasmuch as the school is about 70 to 80 percent Negro and Puerto Rican, of poor background, there is a retarded reading grade level, and arithmetic grade level. There are many children who are what could be called antisocial—actually the more appropriate word is dissocial, in that their behavior is not necessarily accepted by the society's norm. These children breed a tremendous problem which the city denies. I became aware of that in looking through the school at White Plains, where there were relatively few Negro and Puerto Rican children. This may not be an intentional thing. But the fact remains that in New York City the schools are filled with Negro and Puerto Rican children, especially the schools for the deaf.

Much of the problem arises in the family, where these indigent families are not academically oriented. The parents may not know how to, or they may not be able to, communicate with their children, because they speak a foreign language. There may also be the factor of maternal deprivation.

The school should be the opportunity for these children to learn how to adapt or conform to the society in which they are supposed to live and be a part, and also, if possible, develop constructive assets.

As Dr. Grinker pointed out, there is an optimal age at which we can activate or stimulate the subgroups of personality. The optimal age to reach children is obviously during the school years, and especially in our schools—which are really the primary media through which one can reach these children, who are action oriented by their poverty or adverse circumstances or culture. This is true even for hearing children. We are concerned with deaf children, and so it might behoove groups in other cities as well as New York to concentrate on how to communicate with these people, and perhaps establish a more adequate school system which would not permit the current deterioration to continue.

A Plan for a Clinical and Research Program With Psychotic Deaf Patients

Dr. Eugene Mindel

Dr. Mindel:

A 3-year program for psychiatric diagnosis, therapy, and research on the psychotic deaf has been undertaken at the Institute for Psychosomatic and Psychiatric Research and Training, Michael Reese Hospital, Chicago. The project, funded by the Vocational Rehabilitation Administration, has now been in operation for 6 months under the direction of Dr. Roy R. Grinker, psychiatrist.

In their efforts to gain needed experience and knowledge for provision of therapy to deaf persons, the psychiatric and psychological staff surveyed a nearby State hospital for deaf patients. Following identification and careful diagnosis, certain patients were selected for transfer to the institute where they were subsequently seen for intensive study, including group and individual therapy, and complete medical diagnoses (EEG, neurological and audiological evaluations included). All psychotherapy was carried out in sign language without the aid of interpreters. Various techniques of therapy have been tried with resultant hypotheses regarding approaches offering the greatest potential.

Outpatients, referred from police agencies, private psychiatrists, schools, and attorneys, have also been participants in the study. Some of these persons are given treatment while others, after a diagnosis has been made, are referred to different environments.

From this direct in-depth observation of deafness, the staff psychiatrists and psychologists have developed a number of hypotheses regarding factors which lead to mental illness among deaf persons, the role of verbal communication in psychopathology, and the psychological impact of deafness on family structure and parent-child relationships.

All of the project staff have been taught the language of signs to facilitate communication with the patients under study. In addition, other professional staff at the institute, including nurses, resident psychiatrists, social workers, and occupational therapists have taken part in this training.

Project psychiatrists and psychologists have attended clubs for the deaf, religious services, and schools in order to obtain the broadest possible experiential background in terms of normal deaf persons as well as those who are disturbed. As the core staff becomes more fully experienced and knowledgeable about deafness, they will undertake the training of other professional staff at the institute and in the State mental health system.

Members of the project research staff meet periodically in conferences to which research observations, pertinent literature and appropriate consultants are brought. Several papers on developed hypotheses and the role of certain organic factors, i.e., related etiologies of deafness, on behavior are being published.

In an effort to develop means of preventing mental illness in deaf people, a pilot project has been instituted under my direction as a child psychiatrist with the project. Families of young deaf children, referred from the Henner Speech and Hearing Center of Michael Reese Hospital, are seen by me and the psychological staff of the project in a series of therapy sessions. In addition to offering services to the parents and children, it is intended that this pilot project will reveal the basic psychological coping mechanisms which parents of deaf children use in both a healthy and a pathological adjustment to the impact of deafness on the family.

At the present time, plans are being made for the eventual provision of coordinated rehabilitative services for mentally ill deaf persons in Illinois. The proposed program will involve the cooperative efforts of the State Department of Mental Health, the Illinois Division of Vocational Rehabilitation, State hospitals, and speech and hearing staffs in the State system.

Conference Summary and Comments

Dr. Roy R. Grinker, Sr.

Dr. Grinker:

I think I express the view of all of us, when I thank the New York group for furnishing us with such rich fare. Their activities have been inspirational.

There is something fascinating about the way they present their problems. There is something about the way in which they are committed to this field that is very seductive, an experience I had 2 years ago when I visited here and became involved, from that point on, with the deaf program.

The deaf speakers we saw have had a combination of types of communication. Sometimes a speaker would verbalize, and the good Reverend would sign. Sometimes the speaker would sign, and the good Reverend would read his verbal communication. At one time, someone both communicated verbally and signed. I do believe that some sound experimental work could be devised to determine once and for all the controversy regarding the development of oral, sign, or finger-language communications among the deaf. These various opinions are maintained by various educational groups, but with little actual data.

Let me summarize the meeting from the notes that I made. As I go along I will try to raise questions which I hope will not be interpreted as criticisms. But this is a field in its infancy, and I think all of us have to recognize that there are many questions that have to be faced.

Early in the meeting a statement was made that there was a great lack of interest by psychiatrists in the problems of the deaf, and it was stated that psychiatrists become anxious with the forms of communication necessary for working in the deaf field; that probably is correct.

The question is, why are psychiatrists interested now? A good sociological study could be made, I think, of the shifting attitudes in the field. As a corollary to that question, since most of us are involved in some form of training programs, what kind of psychiatrists can work with the deaf?

We are all trying to train people in various fields. It would be better if we knew what kind of people are most adept or most able to be consistent in a particular field. I would be interested to know what kind of psychiatrists can become interested in the deaf. I don't think that it is a question, as Dr. Rainer stated, of creating a subspecialty. I think we have enough subspecialties, and particularly I think it would be ill-advised to create a subspecialty for the study of the psychiatric problems of the deaf, because as we have seen so clearly here, this is an area for multidisciplinary work. We should not allocate onto ourselves the primary positions.

Perhaps one could divide the problems that have been raised at this meeting in terms of (1) service to the deaf, (2) teaching of the deaf, (3) teaching of the people involved with the deaf, and (4) research. But at this stage of the concern with the deaf, these areas are not sufficiently differentiated.

Perhaps I may summarize by differentiating the presentations in an epidemiological sense into those concerned with primary, secondary, and tertiary prevention. All of these problems will raise so many questions, the answers to which are unknown, and all of them require such extensive research, that really, what we are now engaged in, is hypothesis finding.

Let me first take up what is known as tertiary prevention or rehabilitation. The percentage of patients found in State hospitals, if we use the New York system as a prototype, has been said to be 2 percent of the total deaf population, and some of these are involved in mistaken diagnoses.

Casefinding in the State hospitals has been a very difficult problem in New York, as it is in Illinois. Eventually we will have to move out of the State hospitals into the community as a source of our patients, and the problem of casefinding in the community is, as you know, even more difficult. I would also expect, as Dr. Rainer has said, not a decrease or abolition of deaf problems, but an increase, not only because of the fact that virus diseases have not been combated effectively, but also because we are seeing an increased effectiveness of the pediatricians, who save the lives of children with tuberculous and bacterial meningitis, with increasing residues of deafness.

One of the problems in rehabilitation is to tackle the problem of the adult deaf, who can be helped, whose problems can be ameliorated with fresh points of view. I would be loath to see an already developed theoretical approach used for the treatment of the adult deaf. I refer particularly to the standard psychoanalytical concepts, the standard psychotherapeutic processes. I would advise that we concentrate on new ways of dealing with the adult deaf. I think that the general systems theory, which is all-embracing and does not commit one to a particular theoretical approach to parts of the system is the least likely to bring us into error.

It has been stated that group therapeutic processes are effective. Certainly, the groups do decrease the processes of isolation, the habits which have been acquired over the years. They are effective in establishing a relationship with an institution which remains permanent and available for all times.

The diagnostic problem among the adults is one which bothers me a great deal. I have heard so frequently that the diagnosis of schizophrenia has been made. This in itself, as you know, is a wastebasket term, not well defined, and its categories are differentiated only with difficulty.

Perhaps because I have been working with the borderline syndromes for so long I see in many of the problems that have here been presented to us some of the characteristic disturbances in ego functions that we find with the borderline. These are angry people who have a great deal of impulse eruption. They have difficulty in attaining and maintaining affectionate relationships, and they have a great deal of difficulty in establishing stability. Their depression is characterized by loneliness, in that although they try to approach others, they soon are disturbed by closeness and move away, so that they are, indeed, lonely people. One of the things I have found is that diagnosis of chronic, undifferentiated schizophrenia is very frequently really that of borderline syndrome.

The borderline, also, have the same type of mother-child problems in the background—because they suffer from some kind of deficiency in mothering—that we can ascribe to the deaf child, whose maternal relationships are, in general, deficient. Also, they have difficulty in establishing in early life a good relationship with their peers.

With regard to psychological tests, I see a great deal of application of test instruments which are utilized for hearing people. Attempts have been made to give instructions which can be utilized by the deaf. But as Zubin in this institute has reported, the correlation between Rorschach results and clinical findings is not very high unless the Rorschach, as an instrument, is used as the framework for interviewing.[1]

We should attempt to develop instruments which are directly devised, and applicable to the deaf on the basis of hypotheses derived from clinical observations. For example, what Harrower and I de-

---

[1] Zubin, J., Eron, L. D. and Schumer, F. *An Experimental Approach to Projective Techniques.* New York, John A. Wiley, 1965.

scribed as an ego tolerance test, was devised especially for people who were flyers, and was used by us in a modified form in the stress studies on paratroopers.[2] So I would think that one could devise a TAT to elicit the specific emotional problems of the deaf.

It is, of course, a question as to how much can be accomplished in the way of rehabilitation. I think that there are evidences that a good deal of conduct reinforcement, in terms of longstanding group relationships, may have some degree of effectiveness.

One thing that I observed in the group yesterday is that the individuals were almost unintelligible in their speech. Yet when they were stimulated to interjectional speech, heavily loaded with affect, they spoke as clearly as any hearing person. It would seem to me that this is a means by which one could grab hold of some sort of conditioned response.

Another important problem which has been brought up, for example by Mrs. Friedman, is that, while in community activities or in social life it is possible to have any of three worlds, the deaf feel much easier and better working and living in the deaf community. This suggests that we should take a page from the present antipoverty program system, namely the use of indigenous persons to work with the deaf community, rather than people outside of the actual deaf population. If we did use them, I think our activities within the community, both for education and for cooperation, would be much more effective.

The second category, which we could call secondary prevention—that is the amelioration of disturbances before they become fixed and permanent—has been largely affected by school activity. I must say that I was extremely well impressed by the school and the attitudes displayed there, the pupils' attitudes and the attitudes of the teachers and their great interest in the children. But what bothered me about the school was the neatness, the cleanliness, the orderliness, and the odorlessness of a school devised for preschool children. It seems to me to be an artifact which bodes no good for the children's adjustment.

In the school I was impressed by the happy attitude of the children. When these preschool children cried, or when they babbled, I tried to determine whether there was any difference between these sounds and those of hearing children. It seemed to me that the quality of the sounds of crying and babbling are identical with hearing children. They do not have the quality of speech of the adult deaf. This seems to me to point to an area of education, at what we might call the critical period.

---

[2] Harrower, M. R. and Grinker, R. R. The stress tolerance test. *Psychosom. Med.*, 8: 3–15, 1946.

I believe that the critical period at which substitutions or alternative positions for the lack of hearing will have to be instituted is somewhere in the region of 2 years of age. At the same time we must recognize that there are differences in these children. One cannot lump all deaf children together. There are differences in intelligence and certainly there are differences in degree of brain damage, even where there is no gross defect. In cases of minimal brain damage, finer phase studies, with modern electro-encephalographic techniques, can determine the more exact localizations of areas of dysfunction.

It is a fact also that there are constitutional differences in children. That is, some children are auditory, some are visual, and some are tactile. It would become very important to know before one embarked on an education by tactile or visual means to substitute for the auditory technique, whether these children have the capacity to learn concepts by these other methods.

Certainly, there has been a great deal of isolation of the deaf child. There has been a tremendous confusion on the part of parents. Certainly, we have seen denials all over, from the State down to the parents, and even from the children, later on in life.

To overcome the denials, a very extensive educational process is required. We went through the same thing in a number of phases in the development of medicine. For a long time there was a denial of the fact that people had venereal diseases. Until very recently there was a denial that sex produced children, and that sexual intercourse occurred between males and females, and that this act produced children. Now we hear this all the time on radio and television.

All this requires a great deal of public education. We must ask ourselves: Is the group work that has been discussed as occurring with parents of adolescents and latency children too late to effect much improvement in the children? To effect the maximum in improvement, I think that one has to get back to the earliest parental denial.

Now to move toward the subject of primary prevention, which is mostly a research area. It surely requires multidisciplinary activity. For me, the most exciting part of research in this area is that it offers a great opportunity to study the development of ego processes.

When one kind of input is lacking, one can study ego processes better, because, in a behavioral sense, the damage determines ego functions which are missing, and this is one of the characteristic techniques of medicine. We learn about physiology from pathology. We have enough genetic knowledge to surmise where the high-risk group occurs, and so we should be able to pick up these children early, in order to study them and institute what our studies would indicate are proper therapeutic procedures.

In these children at an early age we have tried hard to determine how we can detect the earliest evidences of brain damage. I think this is a tremendously important field for research in relation to the deaf.

Early detection seems to me to be important, because there is a critical period during which concept formation and symbol representation is begun. Beyond that period, when the foundation is lacking, there is less opportunity to compensate for a defect.

Let me tell you what Dr. H. J. A. Rimoldi, who is a distinguished psychologist who has been working all his life in problem solving, states. He feels that the logical structures of the mind are innate; that is, that humans have evolved the kind of thinking which he calls logical structure; that its development begins with language, which is concerned with form, and it may also be with color; and that the same logical structures if properly evoked by these early techniques, may then be expressible in many languages, up to abstractions characteristic of mathematical language.[3] The sound thing, then, for education to use would be the basic language of logical structures.

Another field of research which seems to me to open great avenues has less to do with testing to determine the child's ability, or his IQ, or what he is able to do. It would be, rather, an attempt to educate him as far as possible in symbolic language by reinforcing and conditioning, to approach the deaf child as Goldiamond and Azrin have done with animals—who are speechless—and attempt to condition them by reinforcement as far as they can go.

Dr. Ostwald has brought up in his paper an extremely important concept. Technology has advanced now to the degree where it seems to him—and it seems to me—to be feasible to have alternative ways of putting information into the child's mind. One of our people at Chicago, in fact, is tooling up to develop a visual feedback system by which these children can correct their visual communications.

Let me tell you briefly what else we are doing in Illinois. We would like to imitate the New York system. Unfortunately, we haven't the competent and distinguished personnel to do it with, and so we have to feel our way along.

We have started out by obtaining support from Vocational Rehabilitation Administration for five beds in which to hospitalize deaf patients taken from the State hospital system. Doctors Mindel and Vernon have found the same difficulties as you have in New York in determining where the deaf psychotics are in the State system. Until we can get better communication we're going to have to ferret them

---

[2] Rimoldi, H. J. A. Thinking and language. *Arch. Gen. Psychiat.*, 5 : 568–575, 1967.

out from each hospital. Over the period of a year we would hopefully bring these people into our hospital, and immerse ourselves in the problems of the deaf.

As we are developing research ideas, they will be applied, we hope, through Dr. Mindel's work with deaf children, to understanding the processes of concept formation in them. And as these 3 years of our grant go by, we hope to train personnel to effect a phasing out, which will allow putting the responsibility for the deaf inpatient service and the outpatient service in one of the zone centers of the State. It is quite likely that we will transfer some of our personnel, our aides and nurses, to the State institution. Thereby we will have a continuity of influence, and maintain our own position within the State system. In brief, we go backwards from the direction that you have gone.

I think that there are so many problems that have been brought up at this meeting, all of which have been recognized and the difficulties explained, that we can all go back to our places of origin and apply some of the things we have learned, depending upon the situation that we find at home.

School, 3, 30, 82, 96, 97, 120, 132, 150
  phobia, 80
  programs, 5
    See also Education; Public
      school; Residential schooling
Self-control, 67, 68
Self-image defects, 88, 102, 103
Self-esteem, 128, 129, 130
Separation anxiety, 80, 81
Sexuality, 3, 12, 13, 16, 67, 76, 95, 109
Sheltered workshops, 117
Shipley, Edward, 81, 82
Sign language, 18, 27, 30, 77, 86, 90, 100,
    104, 121, 131, 132, 133, 135, 140,
    142, 145, 147
    See also Finger spelling; Hand
      signs; Manual language
Social isolation. *See* Loneliness
Social work and workers, 31, 37, 117,
    133, 135, 138
Sonnega, James A., 120, 135
Spatial cues, 78
Special classes and schools, 117, 118,
    138
Speech and speech development, 96
    See also Language
Stanford Achievement Test, 129
Stelle, Roy M., 4, 5, 7, 11
Suicide, 82
Summary. *See* Conference summary
Superego defect, 87
Sussman, Alan, 25, 33, 36
Symbolization, 67, 87, 137, 138

TAT, 89, 90, 91, 150
Team. *See* Mental health team
Teenagers, 79
    See also Adolescents
Telephones, 82
Teletypewriters, 127
Television, 18
Temporary N.Y. State Commission to
    Study Problems of the Deaf. *See*
    under New York
Tests, cooperation in, 89
    psychological. *See* Psychological
      testing
    See also under name
Theoretical considerations, 65

Therapy. *See* Group therapy; Psycho-
    therapy; Treatment
Training. *See* Psychiatrists, training
    of,
Tranquilizers, 63, 139, 141
Treatment and treatment program, 95
    See also Psychiatric treatment;
      Therapy
Trifluperazine, 111
Twins, 49, 53, 70, 124

Underemployment and unemploy-
    ment, 33
United States Vocational Rehabilita-
    tion Administration, 3

Vernon, McCay, 152
Violence. *See* Aggression
Virus infections, 118, 148
Visible articulations and speech, 126,
    127
Visual functioning, 81, 93, 124, 141, 152
Vocational adjustment, 33, 115
Vocational counseling and guidance,
    135
Vocational planning, 89
Vocational rehabilitation, 31, 35, 39, 54
    See also under New York; under
      Illinois
Vocational Rehabilitation Administra-
    tion, 118, 119, 145, 152
Vollenweider, John A., 47, 54, 55, 60,
    82, 88, 89, 93, 94, 111
Volunteers, 31, 32

Waardenburg's syndrome, 17
Warm Springs (Mont.) State Hos-
    pital, 139
Wechsler Intelligence Scales, 89, 93,
    137
Wechsler Verbal test, 90
Weinberg method, 69
Williams, Boyce R., 119
WISC Intelligence Test, 129
Withdrawal (social), 82
Withrow, Frank, 16, 67
Women's Club of the Deaf, Inc., 32
Word association study, 76
Written statements, 139, 140

X-ray, 127